BEAR HIS MILD YOKE

BEAR HIS MILD YOKE

The Story of Mary Dyer
a Quaker Martyr in
Early New England

ETHEL WHITE

ABINGDON
PRESS
Nashville New York

BEAR HIS MILD YOKE

Library of Congress Catalog Card Number: 66-21971

SET UP, PRINTED, AND BOUND BY THE PARTHENON PRESS, AT NASHVILLE, TENNESSEE, UNITED STATES OF AMERICA

IN
MEMORIAM

❧

AUTHOR'S NOTE

Mary Dyer was a courageous woman who lived during the important early years of our country's settlement, yet her contribution to our political and religious heritage has never been widely circulated. It is my hope that this book will bring her story to people all across the nation—including a few in Boston who seem never to have heard of this meek but determined woman.

Since some of the early records have burned or crumbled and tombstone inscriptions have weathered, her story must be put together with bits and pieces from various sources, some more reliable than others. Where dates and facts conflicted, I have used those which seemed to fit the story line better; and where there were no facts, I have imagined what might have been logical and appropriate. Although we do not know that Mary Dyer ever kept a journal, we do know that many of the early Quakers and their contemporaries did so; this form therefore seemed most appropriate for presenting Mary's personal views and feelings.

In reading the journal one should keep in mind that in those times the Julian calendar was in use, so the first of the year was March 25, not January 1. The use of numbered, rather than named, months was a Puritan innovation and was used by John Winthrop in his journal as early as the 1630's. Also, in the interest of readability the flavorful old spellings have been modernized. Thus, Ducksburrow loses its identity by becoming Duxbury. But of course the colonists did the same thing, and St. Botolph's Town became Boston!

Now a word about the "plain" language. The use of "thou" for second person singular was common when adults spoke to children, servants, and other inferiors, or close friends and relatives. However, "you" was always reserved not only for second person plural, but also for peers and superiors. (This is readily apparent in foreign languages today where a "polite" form of second person singular is usually identical to the second person plural form.) Then the Quakers came along with their idea that no person was due more respect than another simply because of noble rank or high office—all were children of God and meant to be treated with the same courtesy and kindness, without knee-bending or hat-doffing. They therefore "thou'd" everyone, kept their hats on, stiffened their knees, and suffered grievously for such seemingly harmless practices.

A few times I have used what seem to have been the actual words of certain people. I am sure these passages will be readily apparent to the reader.

Below is a list of books which were especially helpful to me.

Adams, Charles. *The Antinomians in the Massachusetts Bay Colony*, Vol. 21.

Andrews, Charles. *The Fathers of New England.*

Braithwaite, William. *The Beginnings of Quakerism*

Bruce, H. A. *Woman in the Making of America.*

Doyle, J. A. *The English Colonies in America,* Vol. 3.

Earle, Alice. *Home Life in Colonial Days.*

Fiske, John. *The Beginnings of New England.*

Fox, George. *The Journal of George Fox.*

Hale, Edward E. *The Story of Massachusetts.*

Holder, Charles Frederick. *The Quakers in Great Britain and America.*

Hosmer, J. K., ed. *Winthrop's Journal: History of New England from 1630 to 1646.* 2 vols.

Jones, Rufus. *The Quakers in the American Colonies.*

Joy-Dyer, Cornelia. *Some Records of the Dyer Family.*

Miller, Perry. *Roger Williams: His Contribution to the American Tradition.*

Palfrey, John Gorham. *A Compendious History of the First Century of New England to 1875.*

Powell, Lyman. *Historic Towns of New England.*

Richman, Irving. *Rhode Island: Its Making and Its Meaning.*

Sparks, Jared. *Lives of Anthony Wayne and Sir Henry Vane.*

Wish, Harvey. *Society and Thought in Early America.*

God doth not need
Either man's works or His own gifts; who best
Bear His mild yoke, they serve Him best . . .

—John Milton

Sitting in a scarred and battered armchair in the warm sunlight, an old man alternately dozes and reads from a well-thumbed manuscript on his lap. He lets the memories come flooding back, tumbling and spilling over one another like the seething waves along the rocky Narragansett shore. Though his joints are old and stiff, his eyes dim, his spirit weary, he can remember now so many things long forgotten—how sweet, how eager, how very young his dear Mary was when first they fell in love; and how she changed throughout the quarter-century of their marriage, growing more serious and purposeful, until that purpose drew her from him, gradually yet irrevocably. Her journal tells the story. . . .

1635

Boston
Massachusetts Bay Colony
[*Eighth month*] *New England*

How odd it seems to write this heading! But odder things than this are bound to occur, for we have left the old England for the new, to embark upon a great and perilous adventure.

Our arrival in Boston Harbor this morning was quite

as auspicious as anyone could wish. After a fearsome six weeks of being buffeted and tossed about unmercifully by fierce winds and savage seas; of wracking sickness, pain, and death; of dreary and interminable sermons and prayers —after all this our weary little ship, with all her weary passengers, rounded Cape Cod and steered for port.

Recollecting that he had on board wealthy and noble Henry Vane, whose family was known throughout England, our captain stood off from shore long enough to send a small boat scurrying to apprise the colony of its distinguished visitor. Thus forewarned, a group of Boston's most important citizens gathered on the wharf to meet us as a salute of cannon and muskets from the fort heralded our slow approach to anchorage among the outer islands.

I shall always remember my first view of our new home— of the peninsula with its gently sloping meadows, and its three bare, rocky hills drenched by the ocean's salty breezes and looking rather bluish in the smoky autumn haze; and of the mainland where here and there vivid splashes of orange, crimson, and gold brightened the dark green pines which thickly blanketed all the area about the Charles River. Lying at the foot of the protecting hills and stretching almost to the beach was the village, its few houses huddled together as closely as their tiny orchards would permit, and its streets (little more than cow paths) following the contour of the land.

My heart sank for a moment as I contrasted this primitive, somber village with our spacious estate at Glastonbury; and with our more recent elegant town house at Charing Cross in London.

Yet almost instantly I recalled our urgent reasons for embarking on this perilous journey—the widespread prevalence of poverty, disease, and crime due to increased taxation for the support of an extravagant and irresponsible monarch; and the cruel, ruthless persecution of religious dissenters by that fanatical ear-cropper and heretic-hunter, Archbishop Laud. Although many of our friends had fled the country years earlier, our family of Dyers had remained in the peaceful shire of Somerset, where low-lying hills enclosed the fertile fields of grain and fruit, and where herds of dairy cows lowed impatiently at milking time.

One day, however, our tranquil life was shattered abruptly when the king's men arrested Will's older brother and hustled him off to prison. His only crime was that of advising our local priest (a Presbyterian at heart, like so many of our friends and relations) to lay aside his robes and candles, and to dispense with litanies and masses. Yet for this modest attempt to purify his religion of meaningless, superficial, and unfounded doctrines and ceremonies, James was carted to London, with common criminals; and, although he had been knighted by the king's father, he was thrust into a loathsome prison where rats, filth, and brutality abounded.

It was only by arduous searching that Will and his father located him, pale and ill, after three weeks. Father Dyer went at once to Whitehall to seek an audience with the king. Because of his faithful and excellent service to the king's father, he was granted an interview; and as a result, James's immediate release was ordered, the only condition being that he promise to uphold the state religion and cease fomenting dissension. This was of course completely unacceptable to James, and he vowed to remain in prison the rest of his life before acceding to such demands.

Will then took a hand in the matter. Sympathizing as he did with his brother's beliefs, he nevertheless reminded him of his filial duty to their aged father. Will and I, newly married, were about to move to London to oversee the family flour interests there, thus leaving only James to care for his father. It was a bitter decision for James, but he realized it was the only Christian course. We left him at their estate, improved in health, but very low in spirits.

Despite this ominous incident, I soon forgot all about religious differences. Every day in town was busy and exciting—directing the servants, furnishing the house, shopping for new clothes—all these filled my days. In the evenings there were parties, balls, plays, and dinners, and we were even presented at court. Life was all gaiety and laughter—and love, for Will was an ardent husband. And so, a few months after we had settled ourselves nicely in town, I discovered I was to have a child. Naturally I was pleased, but Will's joy was boundless. His first marriage, though lasting many years, had been childless; and as James had never married, this infant might well be the sole heir to the name, fame, and fortune of the Somerset Dyers.

As the summer progressed, however, I observed that Will looked more solemn than he had since James's imprisonment. One day, coming home in mid-afternoon during my nap, he burst out, "My dear, I cannot go on like this!"

"Go on like what?" I asked drowsily.

"Mary, thou knowest I love thee greatly, but I can no longer endure the way we live!"

My eyes opened wide, all sleep forgotten.

" 'Tis the extravagant living, the incessant, inane chatter; but even more 'tis the increasing persecution of thousands of good, devout people for nothing more than expressing their belief that the Scriptures rather than priests are the only infallible guide for life—these things have become intolerable." He must have seen the bewilderment in my eyes, for he added more gently, "I know thou hast enjoyed all the gaiety of social life here, my dear, and thou art only a young girl whose character and beliefs have perhaps not yet been fully formed. Nevertheless, thou wilt soon become a mother, and it is imperative that we decide now what things are important to us and that we take steps to protect and nurture these things for the benefit of ourselves and of our child."

"What other course is open to us, Will?" I asked hesitantly, although I suppose I had already guessed.

"My dear," he said soberly, "I want very much to leave England and go to Massachusetts."

There it was. There was more, of course, about the dangers lurking 'round each dark corner at night because the lower classes were starving, about the callous disregard for life or feeling, about the horrors of plague and disease which entered the houses of even the titled and wealthy, about too much government spending and too high taxes.

"Mary," he said desperately, "I've waited so long for a son. I can't bear to have him grow up in a land where he can't think and act according to his own beliefs, and where he'll be taxed to death. I want him to be free and independent, as we Dyers have always been—until now—and as we shall be again, please God!"

"Of course, Will," I murmured, "whatever thou thinkest best. I'll start the packing at once."

He kissed me, and held me tight for a few moments, then hurried off to make his own preparations.

I had put up a brave and willing front before him; but after he left, I threw myself upon the sofa and burst into tears. I was angry and rebellious at having to give up all my finery, my good times, and my very comfortable life; but even more was I terrified at the lonely, bleak, and dangerous future ahead. The dangers of London faded swiftly before the prospect of red-skinned savages, prowling wolves, and a long sea voyage. Massachusetts! The very name caused me to shudder, and I wept anew.

However, I never mentioned my feelings to Will. During those last weeks he was like a boy, now excited and happy, now thoughtful and worried. He made important decisions offhandedly, and weighed the little ones for days. One day when he came home, I saw that he had cut off his long curly locks; now he looked as much a Roundhead as any other brash nonconformist. It was a reckless, foolish gesture —but a proud one too. "Look, everyone!" the short hair seemed to shout defiantly. "The Dyers mean to be free!" But this was not only a crusade for him; it was a glorious adventure. After years of raising and milling grain, and of deferring to his father and brother, he was about to assert himself and gain his freedom by plunging boldly into the unknown.

Thus it was that he roused me early one morning from a fitful sleep and we set out for our final visit to Glastonbury. The air was close and chill, smoky as always, and a thick fog shrouded our carriage as we drove carefully through the narrow, twisting streets. A light drizzle added to our discomfort. So it was with a sad heart that I watched the strong, solid, quiet buildings fade behind us in the swirling, sodden mists. Even Will's mood was somber for a time.

Once we had left the city, however, the drizzle ceased, the fog disappeared, the sun rose, and our spirits rose also until we were laughing and joking as though on any ordinary journey. Along the wayside, the green trees were crowded with a multitude of twittering sparrows, and wild flowers bloomed profusely; in the fields a slight breeze rippled the ripe heads of grain; and I resolved to banish from my mind all despondency and gloom in favor of courage and cheerfulness during our remaining days in England.

The days sped by all too quickly: We saw old friends, made final arrangements, packed yet more things, and received frequent admonitions and advice. ("Be sure to take plenty of woolens, Mary, 'tis colder there." "Better pack more linens—they're cheaper here." "Don't forget thy tools, Will.")

Will shook his head and muttered about the expense, but I insisted on taking along my lap desk, on which I have penned my thoughts ever since I learned to make my letters, the cradle I slept in as a baby, and the old oak armchair which has been my special possession as long as I can remember. Straight-backed and hard though it be, it has been a refuge, a hideaway, a playhouse, and a school. I have wept there over some punishment received, hidden there from some punishment about to be received, played and pretended there, and read my lessons on my mother's lap there. There I accepted Will's offer of constant and abiding love, and in that chair I signed our marriage contract.

Mother also had Dick Hawkins dig up some of her choicest tulip bulbs for me. Sent from Holland, they not only graced our walks and gardens but provided a source of income as well, for throughout Europe people speculated recklessly on them; one large bulb could be traded for an entire farm, or for a very respectable amount of money. Neverthcless Mother generously gave me enough for a pretty planting and added lilies, lilacs, and roses besides. "To remind thee"—she smiled—"of the English countryside."

"And of a dear, sweet Mother," I cried. "Oh, how I shall miss you!"

"Now, now," she chided gently, "thou must set thy thoughts on higher things than home and family. Remember, my child, there is a heavenly home to which we all hope to return some day."

She was right, of course—I was a wicked girl for doting on gay times and pretty clothes as I did! And, oh, I must learn to give my heart and mind to God, who would be with me still when mortal friends were absent. On the other hand, it was easy for Mother to believe and be good—she had never had any doubts or temptations; but even though I had studied the Bible at her knee and listened attentively—for a time—to many interminable sermons and prayers, I was still utterly confused. If God loved us all, how could he elect some to be saved and others to be damned? How dispense grace to a few? How forgive and make holy those who sinned grievously—and continued to sin—while rejecting those who were continuously devout and saintly? Finally, how could one have free choice, or control his life, if every action were predestined? These knotty questions were far too difficult for me to answer. So I kept them to myself, only drinking in gratefully all the loving admonitions of the family along with the sights, smells, and sounds of the countryside.

At last the day of parting was at hand. "God be with you, my dears," said Mother fondly. "Take care. Write often. Let me know when the baby comes. And don't lose those remedies I've given thee!" So Mother was left with several devoted servants to care for her, and Will's father was left with James; and with them I left half my heart, and all my prayers and good wishes.

We traveled at a leisurely pace, out of respect for my condition, reaching Southampton the next day. Upon arrival we boarded the *Abigail* and set about making ourselves as comfortable as possible in the face of crowded and close conditions, owing not only to the large number of passengers aboard, but also to the equally great number of pigs, cattle, and fowl. When Dick and Jane Hawkins—for they and their three young boys were going with us—had brought all the baggage onto the ship and stored it properly, we all went on deck for a final view of our beloved country.

Standing there at dusk, we watched the gray city drop slowly astern as our ship sailed out of the harbor and into the Channel, and set her course for the crimson- and purple-tinged clouds welling up in the west.

Will squeezed my shoulder sympathetically as I blinked to keep back the tears. "Good-bye to England," he said solemnly. "God grant our new home may be half as fair."

Beside us Jane threw her apron over her face and burst into loud sobs. After a time, however, when we all felt more composed, I bade Will a reluctant good-night and hustled Jane off to the women's quarters. Poor dear—this ignorant, superstitious woman was certainly not an ideal companion. Still, she was better than no servant at all and had been with our family ever since I was a child. Moreover, her husband was a hard-working, sensible man, a welcome addition to an undertaking such as ours. With these thoughts in mind, I comforted her as best I could, being comforted myself in no small measure by the presence of her familiar, homely figure. Presently we gulped a bite of supper and retired for the night.

Thus began our voyage to a new land. While the warm, sunny days continued, I found the journey almost bearable. Our days were filled with numerous tasks—nursing the sick, caring for the babies, mending, knitting, sewing, cleaning. Occasionally I ran up to the deck for a few moments of fresh, exhilarating ocean air, a look at the new baby sheep or calves, and perhaps a brief chat (and a briefer kiss) with Will. Every day there were services by Hugh Peter, William Shepard, or John Norton, the three ministers on board; or discussions of the sermons by some of the leading laymen, such as Will and his newfound acquaintances, Richard Saltonstall, John Winthrop, Jr., and handsome Henry Vane.

As Seventh month came upon us, however, the equinoctial storms made our lives miserable beyond belief. The air in our crowded cabin was fetid and oppressive with the all-pervading odors of sickness and unwashed bodies; washing was strung about to slap in our faces or drip down our necks; the children were underfoot the livelong day, quarrelling and whining now that they could no longer play on deck. Our stomachs rebelled at the constant pitching and tossing of the ship and the monotonous diet of salt fish, salt pork, pease porridge, and hard, dry bread. To complete our wretched days, the sermons became even longer and more depressing; and our nights were sleepless as the *Abigail* plunged and wallowed in the savage seas. Threatened by the gloomy predictions of the ministers ("Repent! Repent or be damned!"), and menaced by the lashing rains, our hearts and limbs trembled with terror, and Jane and I clung together tightly during the long, dark hours of the night.

These ominous events reached a climax one evening when we were about four weeks out from Southampton. The wind had been fitful in the morning, and the sea was sullen under a leaden sky. Toward evening, however, the wind began to rise, whipping the waves into churning mountains and snatching the sails from their masts. Our battered ship plunged doggedly into the gale, which shrieked and whistled about the bare rigging. Rain fell in torrents and terrifying crashes of thunder deafened us. The livestock and poultry pens, though carefully lashed to the deck, now tore loose and skidded from side to side, slamming into the rails with each roll of the ship. Into this devilish tempest three brave men struggled from their cabin to secure the pens from further damage. All three were swept instantly into eternity. No one else ventured out, and we women spent the interminable hours huddled together with the children, who were too frightened even to whimper.

With the dawn came a lessening of the wind and rain, and we set about inspecting the damage. Gone were half a dozen pens of choice livestock and poultry; gone were the sails and one of the small boats, while the mainmast leaned at a dangerous angle. Disheartened though we were at the loss of these material possessions, we felt still more keenly the loss of our three brave companions, whose eager hearts and willing hands were so necessary to the success of our expedition—a blacksmith, a carpenter, and our own Dick Hawkins. Jane and the boys were inconsolable, and I was myself discouraged.

I was also not a little rebellious when the Reverend Mr. Peter exhorted us to believe it was all a direct manifestation of God's wrath and judgment.

Reading from the Book of Job he shook his bony finger at us and warned solemnly, " 'How oft is the candle of the wicked put out! and how oft cometh their destruction upon them! They are as stubble before the wind, and as chaff that the storm carrieth away.' "

This seemed to me a shameful aspersion on Dick's character. I had not known the blacksmith and carpenter well, but Dick Hawkins I had known all my life, and a kinder, more conscientious and upright man never lived. How could the ministers say he was wicked? And why should he have died when others less useful and good were spared?

Will urged me to have more faith. " 'We know that all things work together for good to them that love God, to them who are the called according to his purpose,' " he reminded me. "We know we are the called, Mary, because we have been called from a land of oppression to one where we may worship God as we think he wishes to be worshiped. Furthermore, thou must remember what the apostle Paul said, 'For now we see through a glass, darkly; but then face to face: now I know in part; but then shall I know even as also I am known.' "

"I don't want to know *then;* I want to know *now,*" I sobbed. "Has God deserted us? In separating ourselves physically from the English church have we separated ourselves from him?"

"Nay, my love, 'tis not the wideness of the ocean, nor our withdrawal from any temporal church, which can separate us from our Father; only our proud and sinful hearts can do that. And if we but love him, his strength will sustain us until at last his ways are made plain."

These words comforted me greatly; and I in turn was able to offer some small measure of consolation to Jane.

The remaining days passed quickly and uneventfully as the weather brightened; and it was in the crisp, cool air of early autumn that we at last reached our destination —the famed Massachusetts Bay Colony—, received our salute, and disembarked to begin a new life.

Finally we are settled. Such scurrying hither and yon, such bustling, arranging and re-arranging, such hammering, sweeping, and washing! But now we are settled in our own home. It is a tiny house, to be sure, with only two rooms downstairs and the loft upstairs, yet we thought it best to take what was available rather than attempt to build with both winter and the baby soon to come.

Will has set up our bedstead in the keeping room, attaching it to the wall so that it can be folded up out of the way during the day. Our pots and pans are grouped about the huge fireplace which extends half the width of the room. In front of it we have placed a settee; its high solid back will shut off some of the cold drafts which even now plague us. Along the third wall are the benches and plank table which Will has made; and along the fourth wall are my old oak chair, the spinning wheel, the cupboard for our wooden trenchers and silver, two other chairs, my writing desk, and our chest of clothes. Tucked away in a corner is the cradle, already made up for its new occupant. In the other room are several more chairs, a small table, and Jane's bed. Each room has one small window covered with oiled paper to let in a small amount of light, but these must be shuttered soon. Upstairs the boys have their freshly filled straw pallets and patchwork quilts. Although the boards are roughly hewn and the floor is of hard-packed dirt, Will has plastered all the cracks with clay, and the thick thatched roof will keep us all snug and safe.

Snug and safe I pray we shall be. Our good fortune in acquiring this cottage was only due to the misfortune of its previous owner, who lost his life by drowning during a recent hurricane. Hundreds of trees were blown down on the mainland, while fields and pastures were flooded. (Perhaps it was this same storm which buffeted us so unmercifully at sea?) Other houses stood vacant till now, also mute evidence of the disastrous effects upon the settlers of harsh winters, sickness, and the never ending scarcity of food. Indeed, my neighbor, Mrs. Winthrop, tells me that this is the first season in the four she has been here that the colonists have been able to raise crops sufficient to maintain themselves until spring. Thanks to Will's insistence and foresight, our ship was so well provisioned that we newcomers will not be a burden to the colony, like many of our predecessors.

Our friend Henry Vane has decided to build a house which will be more in keeping with his high position than any now available. In the meantime he will add a sitting room and bedroom to the house of the teaching elder, John Cotton, with whom he is staying. Both ministers appear to be quite as rich as Governor Winthrop, for their houses are nicely finished, spacious, and well furnished, with real glass windows. (Wealthy William Coddington, across the street from the governor, even has a brick house.) Indeed, Mr. Cotton's abode is so large that last year he was able to house another of my neighbors and seven of her children until they could build their own home.

This neighbor, Mistress Hutchinson by name, has been most kind in helping us with our affairs. Scrubbing the linens with me, or stirring a pot of stew, she is so friendly and motherly that already I have lost much of my homesickness and fear of this new land. Did I say she is motherly? She has certainly had the experience for it with fifteen children to practice on! How she copes with her many responsibilities I do not know, but she must be wonderfully capable, for her house is neat and clean, her children well mannered, and she herself a calm, cheerful friend to those in need. Her dignity and forthright manner make her imposing, and although not beautiful, her sturdy figure, dark eyes and hair, and intelligent expression combine to form a most pleasing aspect.

When Will came home today at dusk he brought with him more news of Mr. Cotton. It seems that a Mr. Roger Williams, formerly assistant pastor here but now at Salem, had stirred up a great controversy some months ago by publicly expressing his opinion that the king had no right to deed this land to white settlers without the consent of its Indian inhabitants.

"Nonsense!" cried Salem's Governor Endecott (according to Will). "These people are savages! Besides, this land was claimed by English explorers for the glory of God and of the king."

Mr. Williams was brought before the General Court (the governing body of the colony, consisting of the governor, magistrates, and deputies), admonished, and released. Shortly thereafter, he preached on public sins and religious freedom, inveighing unrestrainedly against the English tax to support ministers and churches, compulsory attendance at services, a religious oath as a prerequisite for holding public office, the regulation of church doctrine—and individual belief—by the civil authorities, and continued alliance of the Bay church with the Church of England.

Now the fat was really in the fire! What he advocated, Will explained, was the separation of church and state. This doctrine is anathema to these settlers, for they firmly believe in the king as head of both religion and government. Moreover, the founding of this bay colony was based on the belief that its settlers were establishing a new Israel, a new chosen people, who would be led by God himself, through his ministers and magistrates.

I could not help feeling a little sorry for the Indians; nor could I help admiring Mr. Williams for his courage in expressing these deeply felt convictions. Will said he was foolish to be so outspoken, but then he grinned wryly and confessed that he had more than a little sympathy with those opinions himself.

Continuing his account, he said that after the pastor's outburst, a shocked and indignant court had met to resolve the issue. They quickly passed a law requiring settlers to swear allegiance to the king and to the civil authorities in all matters.

Mr. Williams refused to swear: "I must be free to follow my conscience in moral and spiritual matters," he said, "however or wherever it lead me."

Today, after months of wrangling and futile attempts at persuasion, the very people whom he had cherished and comforted in their hours of sickness, despair, and loneliness now took to themselves the power of arbitrarily admitting or expelling our colonists and banished this gentle, devout soul to the unendurable hardships of a bitter winter among hostile Indians and savage beasts. At the last moment, however, the court relented and gave him permission to remain in Boston until spring. Then he must leave his friends and neighbors forever.

Will, waiting outside the meetinghouse, saw Mr. Williams as he came out, a man of great dignity, sorrowful yet composed. Rejected and cast out, his manner was still loving and confident, kindly and courteous to all who greeted him; but for John Cotton there was a deeper bow and a special handclasp of gratitude: For Mr. Cotton, although unalterably opposed to the other's views, was the only person in the court who had not voted to banish him.

[*Tenth month*]

A son is born to us—a tiny, healthy, beautiful, utterly lovable baby of our own! He was born yesterday, just before sundown. What a sweet little cherub he is, and so like his father, with fair hair, pink cheeks, and large blue eyes. But mercy! He did put us to a deal of trouble getting here! Will must have paced off ten miles around the room until Anne Hutchinson and Jane shooed him out; and Jane must have slipped a half-dozen of her silly charms under my pillow when Anne wasn't looking. Dear Anne—efficient, composed, gently rubbing my back, bathing my forehead, straightening the rumpled sheets; smiling tenderly as she offered me the tiny, squirming, indignant bundle that was my son—no one could ask for a dearer, kinder, wiser friend.

We have decided to call the baby Samuel, because Will, like the biblical Hannah, has prayed so long for a son and now God has given him one. He will be baptized tomorrow.

Will says if a noisy baptism is a requirement for passage through the pearly gates, they will be standing wide open for Sam. He recounted his version of the ceremony:

"William Dyer," the pastor intoned loudly, "do you promise to bring up this child in the admonition and fear of the Lord?"

"I do," said Will proudly.

Sam began to squirm at all this noise which disturbed his sleep.

"Do you promise to love him and teach him according to God's Word as found in the Holy Scriptures?"

"I do."

Sam was now wide awake and ready to fight for his rights. Clenching his fists and drawing up his legs, he waited tensely.

Mr. Wilson dipped his fingers in the cold water, peered into the baby's face, and said sternly, "Samuel Dyer, I baptize thee in the name of the Father,"—a slight sprinkle, and Sam went into action with a roar which quite startled the minister. He drew back, and then, seeing a few smiles begin to form in the congregation, hurriedly stretched forth his hand again: "and of the Son,"—another sprinkle and a louder bellow from Sam—"and of the Holy Ghost. Amen." He finished with a rush as Sam let loose a third time. "Take him away, Mr. Dyer!" he muttered hastily. "You may be excused from the sermon today. Only take him away!"

And so Will proudly hoisted Sam, still protesting, to his broad shoulder amid the now open smiles of our friends and brought him home to me.

Today I was able to go to church, and of course Sam was a perfect angel. Mr. Wilson glared at him continuously, as if daring him to make the slightest sound, but Sam ignored him and slept peacefully, nestled in my arms through all the minister's preaching and praying. Will looked across covertly at us from time to time, proud and happy; but finally the tithing-man poked him with his long stick and Will quickly turned his attention to the sermon.

I was relieved when the sands ran out in the hourglass for the second time and Mr. Wilson brought his sermon to a close, for I tire easily. Will dropped our offering into the plate and we hurried the few steps home through the snow to our chilly kitchen and cold meal.

"Will," I asked timidly, getting out the food, "dost thou really think God would be angry if we lit a small fire?"

"Now, my dear," he chided gently, "thou knowest the fourth commandment as well as I do: 'Remember the sabbath day, to keep it holy. Six days shalt thou labour, and do all thy work: but the seventh day is the sabbath of the Lord thy God: in it thou shalt not do any work.' Next time be more careful not to let the fire go out."

"I know I was careless, Will, and I'm ready to suffer for my carelessness," I replied meekly, "but I don't want my sweet, innocent little baby to freeze!"

Will looked around in mock alarm. "Sh!" he whispered. "Thou hadst better not let anyone else hear thee call this wee sinner 'innocent.' The church would excommunicate thee faster than thou couldst say 'Governor Winthrop!' Still," he continued, gazing fondly at Sam, "he's not a very big sinner, and I suppose a small fire would not be such a wicked sin—especially if I try hard to do good works this coming week."

He brushed away the crumbs on his face and set to work busily with flint and kindling while I put away the cold venison and bread and stacked the trenchers for washing in the evening.

"There!" he said, dusting his hands. "That will take the chill off. And now, do I get a reward for risking the stocks for thee?" He slipped his arm about my waist and bent to kiss me.

"Nay, nay, Will!" I cried, twisting away with laughter. "Someone might see us. Who will be excommunicated then? Kissing on the sabbath indeed! Besides, thy whiskers are too prickly."

"But, sweetheart," he protested, "we are not permitted to shave on sabbath!"

"I know, my dear," I replied with a sly smile, "but thou'rt not forbidden to shave just before it begins." With this I took up Sam, and settling myself in the old oak chair, hummed a lullaby while he nursed hungrily. Will lounged contentedly on the bed, watching us both with obvious affection.

" 'Tis a good thing yon lad did not arrive a few hours later," he remarked in a few moments.

"Why is that?" I inquired.

"Why, folk here," he said with a twinkle, "think a baby born on sabbath means that nine months earlier on sabbath his parents were not paying as much attention to their prayers as they should have been."

"Thou'rt joking!" I exclaimed.

"Not at all. Only the other day I heard of one of the

poorer ministers hereabouts who had the misfortune to have his latest child arrive on sabbath. In spite of all his protests and explanations and high position, he had to spend his time in the stocks along with the other sinners."

"Gracious!" I said. "Are we to have no privacy from these prying, suspicious people?"

"None, I am afraid," he replied soberly. "As children of God we are all one another's keepers and must hold nothing about ourselves or our neighbors secret but confess our sins and theirs publicly."

Since Sam had finished his meal, I lifted him to my shoulder and patted his back until he belched loudly. He started, looked about drowsily, then let his head fall back.

"Come along, my dear," said Will more cheerfully, throwing my cloak around my shoulders and tucking a thick shawl about the baby. He picked up the foot warmer and we started back to the meetinghouse for afternoon services. I sighed happily as we trudged along. How lucky I am! I have a good husband, kind friend, faithful servant, and a healthy, beautiful baby of my very own. I can think only of the twenty-third psalm: "My cup runneth over. Surely goodness and mercy shall follow me all the days of my life."

Christmas has come and gone. Of course there was no cessation of work, for celebrations of holy days, like the names of the days and months, are now deemed pagan relics from the days of ancient and licentious Rome. Furthermore, since such festivities are encouraged by the Roman Church, we Puritans must eschew them rigorously.

Still, I can remember when I was a little girl and Puritanism was not so widespread that Christmas was quite a different day. Then all our relations streamed into Glastonbury for feasting and laughter. We even exchanged little gifts. Now we give thanks for Christ's birth only in our hearts, or in the dreary, cold meetinghouse, where it is difficult to be thankful for anything.

What a fright I had today! Elizabeth Wilson, the pastor's wife, busybody that she is, informed her husband, and he the governor, that we had built a fire on sabbath last week. Her sharp eyes and my carelessness nearly sent Will to the stocks. He was called before the magistrate; and although he protested stoutly that the sabbath was made for man and not the other way 'round, the magistrate thought otherwise and declared Will guilty. Fortunately, however, since we are prosperous gentry, he only fined Will ten shillings.

I have often been thankful for our rank and riches, but never more so than at that time. The poor artisans and farmers who cannot afford to pay the fine must serve their time on the green near meetinghouse, locked in stocks or pillory, subject to public ridicule.

Will has been admitted to the colony as a freeman, after presenting his credentials and financial statement; and to the church after relating a satisfactory personal religious experience to the clergy. I have been admitted too, but only because Will vouched for my good character and background; I have never had any experience which I could honestly say revealed God's person or Word to me.

1636

[*First month*]

Now it is New Year's day. I always wonder just why this twenty-fifth day was chosen, and what it really signifies, as few people agree on its origin. Some say that God created the world on this day many years ago; others say that our Lord was crucified for our sins on this day and thus inaugurated a new life of hope and promise for all who believe in him. Still others hold that on this day Christ arose from the tomb, assuring his followers not only of forgiveness for sins but also of life everlasting.

But why do I waste my time pondering the far-off past when I cannot even understand what occurs in the present? Mr. Roger Williams, brave soul that he is, has fled the colony. Receiving information several weeks ago that he was negotiating with Indians for land to the south, the court prepared to seize and imprison him. Some of his loyal friends, however, secretly warned him, and he escaped. May God help him through this cold and snowy winter!

When the General Court, with all its so-called men of God, can expel from the church and from society one of the noblest and most pious of men, for a difference of opinion over civil matters, the future holds little promise of security for any of us. If it were not for Anne Hutchinson's comforting presence, I too should experience the despair which envelops many of the women here.

In an effort to combat our dismal surroundings, the deadening routine, and the morbid introspection we are all required to perform, Anne began some time ago to hold weekly meetings at her home for all the women who could attend. After listening on sabbath to the ministers preach their interminable, pessimistic, and often incomprehensible sermons and pray their humiliating hour-long prayers (so persistently that even God must weary of them!), and then wrangle over the same details on Lecture day four days later, it is a blessed relief to hear Anne retell the sermon in her own words so that all of us can understand the message. We even have a chance to ask questions and discuss the difficult passages, something we are never permitted to do in church, thanks to the apostle Paul: "Let your women keep silence in the churches. . . and if they will learn any thing, let them ask their husbands at home. . . ."

Ask their husbands indeed! Some husbands cannot begin to approach the intelligence of their wives; and even Will is sometimes confused over doctrine. Now, however, we can bring our knitting, sewing, or quilting, and work together while we also learn. Anne's expositions are so brilliantly clear that some of the men have begun to attend—Harry Vane, Mr. Cotton, and Will among them.

What a blessing this Anne is to the entire village! She ministers not only to our spiritual needs but also to our physical requirements. Of late I have accompanied her on her errands about the town into homes where misery and illness dwell, where wailing youth enters as sighing age departs; and where broken bones mend faster than a broken heart. She dispenses comfort, cheer, and wisdom to all of us; and we in turn sing her praises to each new ear.

[*Fourth month*]

Messages from Roger Williams indicate that his situation has improved considerably of late. Although suffering greatly because of his illness and the bitter weather, he made his way by degrees and with the help of Massasoit to an Indian camp in Plymouth Plantation, there to rest and recover. From there he proceeded to the head of Narragansett Bay in order to help the Indians. He has decided to buy land to provide shelter for other Englishmen distressed in mind and conscience.

They say there are numerous springs, lakes, and streams throughout the area; and while much of the soil is sandy at the bay and rocky toward the ridges, still it is suitable for fruits and vegetables, and there are grassy islands and meadows for corn and pasture. A big, lush island in the bay will be used as grazing land for goats and pigs. Oak and cedar grow thickly toward the Seekonk River, which teems with salmon, clams, and oysters more delicious than our own; and in the forests fowl, deer, and other game abound.

Because of all these "Providences of the Most Holy and Only Wise," as he calls them, and because the land was "providentially" unsettled, Mr. Williams has named his colony "Providence Plantations." May the hand of God continue to guide and protect him, and extend his influence throughout the colony.

[*Fifth month*]

Thomas Hooker has broken with us on the matter of church government and taken his little flock to a place south of here called by the Indians "Connecticut." He thinks the church should be an independent body, and that the people have a right to decide who shall be magistrates and what powers they shall have. Naturally his views are contrary to the prevailing opinions here.

Time passes so quickly. Each day is filled with activity from sunrise to sunset, and in spite of Jane's great energy and strength there is really more than two of us can do. I tumble into bed at night exhausted, while Will reads a while by the dim light of the smelly fish-oil lamp hooked to his chair.

Besides the ordinary routine there is the huge monthly washing to do, boiling the clothes and linens outside in the iron kettle, drying and bleaching them in the sun, then smoothing them with the heavy wooden rods. There is soap-making, with its sickening odor of hot fat and lye; goose-plucking, with down filling our nostrils and the geese struggling violently until their heads can be thrust into the basket, when they will stand quiet; tedious hours of carding greased wool; drying and salting the prolific, cold-eyed cod; baking huge supplies of rye-and-corn bread once a week; and spinning, spinning, spinning.

It is a blessed relief to take the bucket to the well once or twice a day and spend a few restful moments chatting with our friends. Even Margaret Winthrop brings her bucket, not, I suspect, to fetch water, for her servants can do that, but to gossip with the rest of us. One morning a few months ago she invited Will and me to sup with them. I could hardly wait to see her house, which from all reports was elegantly and expensively furnished.

Indeed, it is so. Not only is the interior paneled smoothly, but the floors are of wood, and the furniture, draperies, and rugs are of the finest materials and craftsmanship straight from London. On the walls are portraits of the Winthrop ancestors, all looking stern, pious, and dull. There is, however, one painting which brought an ache to my heart. It is unmistakably a view of the English countryside, and it brought such a rush of tears to my eyes that I could restrain my emotions only with the greatest difficulty. Upon peering closer, I found that it is a view of Groton Manor in Suffolk, the estate which the Winthrops had reluctantly but dutifully given up at the call of religious scruple.

"What a lovely home you have, Margaret!" I exclaimed, gazing about in some awe at the extravagant number of candles flickering throughout the rooms.

"Thank you, my dear," she replied. "We do enjoy it immensely, but oh, mercy, how expensive it all is—servants, livery, furnishings—and the house not even paid for!"

"Indeed?" I murmured in surprise. "But I thought. . . ."

"That we were very wealthy, just as everyone else thinks," she sighed. "To be sure, we were quite well off in England, in spite of taxes, but John has had severe losses since coming here. You know, if any ship sinks anywhere on the Atlantic Ocean, it is certain to be one in which John has a large investment. Furthermore, he has such an exaggerated notion of the prestige of the governor's office that he would not be satisfied with a more modest home. Ah, well"—she smiled, lowering her voice—"perhaps now that Harry Vane has been chosen governor, John can attend more closely to his own affairs." She drew my arm through hers as we approached the men and whispered, "Please don't mention the election to him. He's still a trifle piqued over it."

I nodded, reflecting that it was small wonder. Harry Vane, only three or four years older than I, had been here barely six months; yet in that time his handsome looks, pleasing personality, and intelligence had acquired for him such popularity that he had been elected to our highest office over such mature and experienced men as Dudley, Coddington, and Winthrop, the last of whom had no doubt begun to think he had a monopoly on the position.

As our host escorted me into the brightly lit dining room, his four children trooped after us and stood patiently around the board below the large silver salt cellar until we had seated ourselves. The board was spread with snowy linen; there were pewter mugs and silver spoons at each place; and at Mr. Winthrop's place there was an additional eating piece—his silver fork, famous throughout the colony as it is the only one there. But amidst all this opulence I saw that the trenchers were common wooden ones like our own.

The servants carried in huge platters of roast turkey, salt cod, and boiled ham; and equally large bowls of baked and boiled beans, squash, turnips, parsnips, onions, Indian pudding, and honey; and plates of rye and Indian bread, and dried apple pie. The little boys drank milk, but of course the rest of us had ale. The boys fell to eating greedily after we had all been served and listened quietly as we discussed the events of recent weeks.

"I wonder how Mr. Roger Williams is faring in his new home," I ventured.

Mr. Winthrop turned his calm eyes toward me and smiled slightly. "You were impressed by him, were you not, Mistress Dyer?"

"Indeed I was," I affirmed stoutly. "In the short time we were acquainted I came to admire not only his courage and piety but also his warmth and kindness."

"Perhaps you came to accept his religious and political tenets as your own, too," he suggested.

Will glanced warningly at me but I felt impelled to speak up.

"I certainly find nothing so wicked in them as to warrant his expulsion from the colony," I said rashly. "And indeed, I cannot help believing still that to banish him was an act of unmitigated cruelty contrary to the principles and spirit of Christianity. Although of course," I added placatingly, "my understanding and wisdom cannot approach that of the ministers and of yourself, Sir."

Mr. Winthrop sighed heavily, while Will scowled fearfully and Margaret looked somewhat apprehensive. Then, in a tone of mild reproof, he replied. "Much of what you say is true. Mr. Williams is a man of exceptional intelligence and godliness. But consider this, please: We are all Anglicans here, bound to our mother church by ancient doctrines although separated by vast distances.

"What is our quarrel with the church? The use of the cross and the surplice, kneeling for this and that, masses in Latin, and tax support for a sometimes ignorant and greedy priesthood. For our nonconformity in these practices we fled our native land, hoping here to worship in simplicity and sincerity with our own educated teachers. We have not altered our fundamental belief in the sovereignty of God, to whom we owe all glory and honor, and but for whose graciousness, justice, power, and truth we would be nothing in the life to come.

"Yet what would Mr. Williams have us believe? He would have us believe that baptism is only for believers—for those old enough to understand their religious beliefs—and then only by immersion, contrary to our old beliefs and customs; that no one should be compelled to attend any church; that the people's chosen priests should have no power over the civil authorities; and that our noble, educated king holds no title to this land.

"This colony, Mrs. Dyer, was not settled by adventurers, unbelievers, and criminals to escape the obligations and just punishments of their native land, but by respectable and hard-working people, so devoted to God that they followed him out of the comfortable cities into the wilderness, there to found a community pleasing in his sight. This is a colony established by godly men for godly men.

"Therefore it is not only our right but our duty to prescribe religious tests for public office so that no unbelievers may control any part of our lives; it is our duty to compel church attendance so that all may have the benefit of divine worship and none may fall into sinful ways through lack of hearing the Word; it is our duty in this church-state so to intertwine our religious life with our civil life that no one can doubt the divine source of our temporal power. And it is our duty to support our noble monarch above the claims of rude, ignorant, and half-naked savages.

"When, therefore, a reckless, impetuous, immature young man challenges the duly constituted authorities, he is, no matter what his motives, guilty of subversion and for the common good must be banished before his dangerous doctrines bring some harm to the community." With this he took up his fork and first examined, then speared his meat as energetically as if each chunk were a dangerous preacher in disguise.

I was at a loss for words. It all seemed so clear and logical when he explained it, yet I could not help feeling that some important element was missing in this kind of government and religion. My thoughts were interrupted by our host.

"As for your question about the welfare of Mr. Williams, he seems to have settled safely in an advantageous location, he and his twenty followers." He frowned for a moment at the thought of these confused souls whose minds had been poisoned by Mr. Williams' rash pronouncements, then went on. "They have established a town on the river at the head of Narragansett Bay. There is good fishing, the land is fertile, and the Indians are friendly. You did not know, I suppose," he said, turning to gaze intently at me, "that Mr. Winslow of Plymouth and I were largely responsible for encouraging the refugees to settle there? We had visited both sides of the Seekonk River and thought the far side infinitely superior. Besides," he added with what passed for a brief smile, "we hoped the river would serve as a barrier to their heresies. We so advised Mr. Williams, and he was, in this instance, pleased to accept our advice along with a few pieces of gold."

I was astonished. Here was a man who had done all in his power to cast out a friend and neighbor; yet only a few weeks later he was helping him secretly to establish a home and an adequate means of livelihood. Had anyone known of this, he would have been severely criticized. I blushed with embarrassment, while Will laughed aloud at my discomfiture, and Margaret tactfully turned the conversation to another subject.

We spoke of the attendance of the Winthrop boys at Master Pormort's Latin School; of the recent founding of a college near the river, although the court's miserly grant of £400 is not likely to build an institution anything like Oxford or Cambridge; of the transportation difficulties between Boston and some parts of the mainland, except at low tide, when the mud flats to Duxbury can be crossed more or less safely and comfortably; of the arrival of Anne Hutchinson's brother-in-law, John Wheelwright, to preach; of John and Priscilla Alden and their eleven children at Plymouth, together with the Bradfords, the Brewsters, and the Winslows; and of the cruel murder of John Oldham by the Pequod Indians. (This last incident was likely to have grave consequences, according to our host.)

One other topic we barely touched on—the news that under Mr. Cotton's prodding the General Court had ordered some magistrates chosen for life. This seemed to me a most unwise move, but having initiated one argument already during the evening, I had no desire to initiate another and so let the gentlemen discuss it perfunctorily.

When we had completed our meal, we all rose, the gentlemen and boys removed their hats, and our host gave thanks:

"Almighty God, we do thank thee for this good food which thou hast so bountifully bestowed upon us for the nourishment of our bodies; and for the friends gathered here with us for the nourishment of our hearts. We do thank thee for these wives and children in good health and for those who have gone on before us [thinking of the son who drowned shortly after their arrival, and his first two wives]; and we do thank thee for all thy many blessings in this strange and savage land. May all our thoughts and actions be determined by thy will and for thy glory. In Christ's name. Amen."

When we had left the board, Margaret showed me the quilt she was piecing, a magnificent blazing coverlet of the Rising Sun pattern, which will soon be ready for quilting. She promised to invite a number of our mutual friends in for a bee within the month.

Then, as I turned to rejoin the gentlemen, she shyly brought out her lap desk and from it took a thin sheaf of papers covered in a tiny, neat script. I glanced over them curiously. To my surprise I found them to be poems of her own making. My admiration and affection for her increased immeasurably at this revelation of her talent and character, for the poems showed an even more sensitive and sweet nature than the affable, pious, and helpful aspect she presented to the critical gaze of the world.

Shortly afterwards Will and I took our leave and strolled back to our plain little home, so poorly furnished with material possessions, yet so richly furnished with gentleness, kindness, and love.

[*Sixth month*]

I have been reminded again that happiness is only transitory, and that the ways of godly men are sometimes strange indeed.

As we feared, the murder of Mr. Oldham had serious consequences. Canonicus, chief of the Narragansetts, hearing that his tribe was accused of the crime, visited Governor Vane in person to assert his innocence and to offer assistance in seeking revenge. The Pequods in turn sought an alliance with Canonicus. At such ominous news Boston sent a hasty plea for help to Roger Williams, requesting him to prevent the alliance; for he had taught and ministered to the Narragansetts in their own language, had bought his land from them with trinkets and gifts, and in all ways treated them as honorable people. Of course these actions won him their lasting respect and love.

Now Mr. Williams, castigated, scorned, and harried by mighty Boston, nevertheless repressed any ill will he might well have felt and set out alone by canoe in the midst of a storm to talk with his friend. Canonicus, an intelligent though unlettered man, realized the inevitability of the white man's settlement of his land, and also the commercial gain to his tribe from this settling. He therefore pledged his warriors to Boston's cause and instructed Mr. Williams on how best to war against the Pequods.

Although there were one or two voices heard in Boston counseling caution and forbearance, the noisy, reckless cries of violence prevailed, and the calling of all able-bodied men for a military expedition began a few days ago. This seems to me the first step in a terrible, mistaken policy of revenge, for the plans are not only to fine the whole tribe the sum of 1,000 fathoms of wampum but also, if it is not paid, to slay all the Pequods!

I was aghast, therefore, when Will volunteered his services and undertook to train the new recruits.

"Will Dyer!" I protested. "How canst thou even condone this wicked action, let alone actively further it? Why, 'twill be nothing but a merciless, inhuman massacre of innocent people who had no part in Mr. Oldham's murder. Why can not Harry Vane meet with the Pequod chief and seek his help in finding those guilty of the crime? Then they can be punished and the others spared. Thou knowest this expedition is cruel and evil, Will. It can only lead to worse relations with the Indians."

"Nonsense, my dear," he scoffed. "Thou knowest naught of such things. This is woman's talk—softness and mercy toward savages! Such a policy would have *us* at *their* mercy in no time, with all of us men slaughtered and thee and thy friends slaves. No, Mary, strong action now, however harsh it may seem to thy tender heart, is the only course which will guarantee us security from future attacks.

"And what of Sam?" he said, his voice and features softening. "The hopes and dreams of half my life are gathered together in that little bundle, and I do not propose to see them destroyed because of a misguided sense of kindness toward ignorant, godless savages."

"Godless!" I burst out. "Of course they are godless when no one will take the time or trouble to even inform them of God. Of all the Christians here only Roger Williams has cared enough to befriend them and teach them, although this teaching was stated as one of the reasons for founding the colony. And thy love for Sam! Surely thou wilt not deny that the Indians also love their children and deserve an opportunity to raise them according to their hopes and ambitions, even as thou desirest?"

But Will was adamant; he who was always so kind and gentle toward all had now taken up the Pequod war as a personal crusade for the sake of his son. Toward a few of our friends who refused to bear arms he maintained a disapproving and cool manner; at home our relations were more severely strained. It was with feelings of both exasperation and anxiety that I watched the small band under Captain Endecott set off on their first military venture, marching into such dangers and horrors as I could only guess.

[*Seventh month*]

Miantonomo, the Narragansett chief, and several of his braves appeared in town today, creating a great stir and not a little fear in spite of the musketeers accompanying them. Jane, seeing the Indians saunter along the street, snatched up the musket Will had left for us and thrust its barrel out the open window, although she had no more idea of how to discharge it than I have. Fortunately one of the children had scampered to Harry Vane's house immediately when the Indians appeared, and our young governor shortly advanced to meet them, greeting them with dignity and courtesy. They retired to his house for a lengthy conference, and it was much later that we learned Miantonomo had signed a peace treaty with England at the conclusion of the meeting. This is the same tribe that has been so friendly and helpful to Roger Williams at his Providence Plantations.

[*Eighth month*]

The mighty warriors have returned! I am thankful indeed that they all escaped injury and disease, yet I fear this adventure has only whetted their appetite for vengeance.

Marching from Boston to Block Island, they killed a few Indians there and then continued to the mouth of the Connecticut River and Saybrook and thence home, burning and plundering as they came and leaving other colonists at the mercy of the now fully aroused savages. The weather is turning cooler now, and the crops must be harvested before frost; therefore the soldiering has been halted until spring. Heaven grant that the snowy winter winds may cool the crusading ardor of these contrary, stubborn men!

[*Twelfth month*]

Little Sam is now over a year old. It hardly seems possible. Indeed it seems only yesterday that he was a tiny babe in arms, content to lie quietly in his cradle. Now he is a big strapping boy in toddling "sleeves" and getting into more mischief than a lad twice his age. All the mothers here use the sleeves as we did in England, as aids in teaching their youngsters how to walk; but alas! the beautiful slashed and embroidered gowns and dresses which are so stylish in England have been outlawed by the general court as too worldly, and although we are permitted to use any old ones we have on hand, we are forbidden to buy any new. I have had to return all the lovely new things Mother sent for Sam. It does seem decidedly presumptuous and meddling of the court to interfere in such personal matters as dress, but Will says it is necessary to keep us a godly community. As a consolation he has promised to buy me some oranges, limes, and potatoes when the next ship from Bermuda docks. Unfortunately everyone is in such an uproar that there may not be any docking or shipping at all, or milling or carpentering or anything, in Boston, all because of John Wheelwright.

Forty-four-year-old John is a lifelong friend of Anne's and relation by marriage. Educated at Cambridge, he is a sincere, upright, courageous nonconformist who came to Boston in Fourth month. There was a strong effort made to appoint him pastor here, but Mr. Winthrop thwarted this action. From here John went to Mt. Wollaston, not far off, for his pastorate. Being highly regarded all about, he was invited to give the Fast day sermon here a few days ago (the fast decreed by the magistrates because of the wretched spiritual condition of believers in Germany, England, and America).

The weather Sabbath day was sharp, and of course the meetinghouse was nearly as chilly inside as out, with its bare walls and floors. The men huddled on one side in their jackboots, many-caped coats, and muffs, while we women fared somewhat better on the other side in our mittens and hoods, and toasted our feet on the foot warmers, although our perches were rather precarious on the backless benches. The elders and deacons faced the congregation on their slightly raised platform, John Cotton with them in his hood, greatcoat, and gloves. The magistrates and governor, full of dignity and authority, sat apart while the poorer folk and servants arranged themselves at the back of the meetinghouse.

Cold though we were, we had not been assembled many minutes before the air became heated with John Wheelwright's invective and castigation. Such denunciation of a congregation I have never heard before. Standing on the platform, near the table on which lay his Bible and a few notes, he thundered accusations at us, gesturing forcefully with his hands as he graphically described our terrible future unless we repented and mended our ways. He urged us to forsake the prevailing but false notion that good works will save our souls, and to substitute for it the newly discovered truth of salvation by grace alone.

Now and again he stalked across the platform like an avenging angel, then turned and slunk back, imitating us miserable sinners. What Philistines we were, he exclaimed, gossiping and criticizing, and groaning over everyone else's sins, and even killing our Indian neighbors for vengeance' sake.

"There are a few believers in Boston," John cried, "who give the appearance of holiness, but ah! [shaking his long finger menacingly] they are all the more dangerous. 'Tis not peace and quiet we must seek, but God's truth! We must be meek, yet fight for our beliefs; be faithful, yet question; live in the Light, yet die for that Light if need be. Those who have the presence of Christ," he concluded, "are happy, though they lose all."

Anne amended this in her brilliant recapitulation two days ago to explain that people who believe in a covenant of *works* go about doing good so they may get into heaven while thinking anything they like; but those who believe in a covenant of *grace* are already assured of heaven as children of God and go about doing good because they are inspired by right intent and an agreement not only to act correctly but to think correctly. Anne said, "If thy mind is right, thine actions will be right."

She also scoffed at the prevalent notion that the death of a child here, where children are so greatly coveted, is a sign of God's wrath. "Nonsense!" she declared. "Sickness is a result of either wrong living or accident, and the cure is to obey the laws of nature. Be clean—all animals clean themselves of their own accord. Eat the right foods—but not too much. Be cheerful—even the birds sing and cats purr. And if thou hast committed no great sin, do not waste thy time trying to dig up a little one in thy mind. Think of other people, do things for them, let them help thee, and keep busy in worthwhile projects; then there will be no opportunity for sinning."

Anne herself is very good with the sick, particularly children, and has healed several almost miraculously. A few of the other women, some jealous, some ignorant, are whispering that while Anne's helper at her right hand is Mrs. Dyer—since I often accompany her—, the one at her left is the arch fiend, Satan himself. Anne shrugs off this gossip impatiently as prattle too trivial to bother about, but I have an uneasy feeling that she is becoming involved in controversial matters.

When I mentioned this to her, she smiled indulgently, patted my cheek, and said, "My dear, thou art a sweet girl to worry about me, but thy fears are groundless. The gossip of busybodies cannot touch me, nor deter me from my duty to the sick; and what harm can come to me from teaching the covenant of grace, when John and I derived it from so eminent and indisputable a source as Mr. Cotton himself?"

This of course was unanswerable. I let the matter drop, but my uneasiness persisted.

1637

[*First month*]

Oh, what a trying month this has been! Will and the other soldiers went off with Captain Mason on another sortie at the first hint of spring, as the Indians have been taking revenge for the cruelties Endecott inflicted on them in the fall. I did not plead with Will this time, nor argue with him. I merely watched his preparations quietly; and after he marched off, I sat down in my old chair and wept unrestrainedly. How can a husband and wife, so close on most matters, be so far apart on others? Things will never be the same between us. I loved him as a man; I looked up to him as a father; my love for him was boundless, my trust implicit, for I thought him all-powerful, infallible. Alas! I have discovered that he is only mortal after all, with mortal failings. How sad it is to know that the glorious joy of our first years has ended; yet one must go on, and I shall try to be a good wife and mother in spite of this heartrending disappointment.

It is extremely selfish of me to dwell on my own troubles when those of my friends are so much greater. The General Court met only yesterday; and after wrangling most of the day about John Wheelwright's Fast day sermon, they finally reached a decision: Contrary to the feeling of most of the church members and some of our most respected leaders—Coddington, Aspinwall, Vane—they have found John guilty of sedition and contempt of the civil authorities!—sedition because he decried all the leaders (who believe in a covenant of works), and his impassioned words might thus cause some stupid fellows to think the leaders ought to be replaced; contempt because the Fast day had been ordered to decrease the differences among us, whereas John has increased them. Harry protested vehemently, I understand, but was outvoted.

It is unbelievable; and yet, when I recall gentle Roger Williams the reasons for this action become clear. This is the theocratic state, acting to preserve its authority as unquestionable and infallible according to its legalistic Old Testament, but without any semblance of the Christian spirit taught us in the New Testament. It is a state which can brook no criticism of the decrees handed down from on high by its magistrate-priesthood. Even Mr. Cotton is not immune: He was charged to explain his position on sixteen theological points, only half of which he proved satisfactorily! So he must watch his step now, or he will be next.

My heart aches for Anne and John, for I believe they are right; my soul is stifled by the oppressive and dreary soul-searching required of us, and the spying and reporting of misdemeanors by one's neighbors in the name of righteousness. Is this the Promised Land, the New Jerusalem? Methinks the elders of our colony are little different in their nature and methods from the cruel and relentless bishops of Old England!

[*Second month*]

My dear Will returned yesterday for a few days in order to prepare the fields for planting and to see that all is well at the mill and the shop, for I have no head for business and should have everything muddled in a trice if it were left to me.

I stood in the doorway waiting for Will, eager to see that he was well and unharmed, yet reluctant to welcome him home because of our differences. To my amazement, he did not bound up the path and fling his arms about me as he usually did. Instead, he approached soberly and embraced me tenderly, saying softly how glad he was to be home again. In a few moments we went inside, where I sat on his lap and stroked his hair gently. It was then that he began to account for this extraordinary behavior.

"Mary," he said solemnly, his voice trembling with exhaustion and emotion, "I have never seen anything so horrible, so cruel, as our battle against the Pequods. It has cured me forever of believing this is the way of dealing with the Indians. Hereafter we must find ways of living in peace with them.

"Captain Mason led us well," he went on after a time, "bravely, but perhaps not so wisely. Our little band of ninety joined Uncas and his eighty Mohegans, and Captain Underhill and his twenty men, at Providence. There we were received by Roger Williams, who urged us to be firm yet merciful. Ah," Will sighed, "how I wish we had heeded his advice! We passed it off, however, vowing that revenge, not appeasement, was our goal.

"Having rested overnight, we set off down Narragansett Bay in the war canoes which Uncas had provided. At Niantic we found Miantonomo waiting for us with his braves and more boats. Rounding the point, we bore westward toward the mouth of the Mystick, whence the Pequods had retreated from Block Island. When we were only a few miles from our goal, we entered a small cove to wait for the protection of night before embarking on the final stage of our sortie.

"Several hours later we were quietly drawing our canoes up onto the beach within hailing distance of the Indian fort. The night was very dark, with black clouds overhead to shut out the moon and stars that would have betrayed us. The wind had risen steadily after sunset and was now rushing and howling through the treetops, which bent and swayed continuously. Behind us the waves crashed along the rocky shore; ahead all was quiet. Creeping stealthily forward, we surrounded the fort.

"At daybreak we stormed the gate and walls, firing volley after volley from our muskets. The sentries were powerless to prevent our advance, and the hapless slumberers beyond awakened only to fall into eternal sleep. Ah," he said sadly, stroking my hair, "it was a terrible sight—the braves starting from their beds in terror, the women and children screaming as the fire licked their limbs, the voracious flames of our brands leaping from tent to hut and blazing against the gray sky.

"It was finished quickly. Then there were only the smoke and stench of death in our nostrils, and the moans of the dying in our ears. Even the wind was stilled. The battle was a complete success for us—and a horrible slaughter for hundreds of Pequods. Even Captain Underhill, a military man accustomed to war, was shaken at the ruthless and cruel action of our men, for he said to me privately, 'Should not Christians have more mercy and compassion?' We lost only two men, however, with twenty wounded, and even they were able to make the return march, driving the few captives before them and flaunting the bloody scalps and hands which hung from their belts for the bounty which the court has authorized.

"And so we came back, burning any Indian village we

came upon, and showing the inhabitants no mercy, making no attempt to determine if they had had anything to do with the murder of John Oldham. Our policy was to kill any or all Pequod men, and enslave the women and children.

"Passing through Providence Plantations on our way home, we informed Mr. Williams of the battle. He too was horrified and declared that he would protest strongly to Governor Winthrop about the butchery. While there I prevailed on him to accept some of the Indian women and children as servants. He was reluctant until I pointed out that he could not only instruct them, but also free them later for independence or for adoption into other tribes, as is the custom. With this in mind he took several of these wretched creatures into his own wigwam shelter.

"God help us!" Will concluded brokenly. "We shall never cleanse our hands of this blood."

I comforted him as best I could; yet it was evident when he left several days later that this dreadful experience had not only stirred him deeply but even destroyed his confidence in the wisdom and righteousness of the colony's leaders.

[*Sixth month*]

Summer has engulfed us in its brilliant, inescapable sunshine. In England, summer days were long and lazy and quiet. I used to lie on the sweet-smelling grass and read or dream, or gaze at the fat little clouds sailing overhead and watch them change into all sorts of fascinating creatures—knights, dragons, fair maidens, ferocious animals. I heard the drowsy chirp of sparrows or the constant humming of busy bees darting from one fragrant flower to another, or the faint soft lowing of the placid cows; I felt the cool breezes gently touch my cheek and heard them rustle the leaves. There were long walks in the woods to hunt for berries and flowers, or along the quiet lanes to feel the dust between my toes. There was a soft haze which veiled the sun thinly and gave a peculiar dreamlike quality to the sunniest day, not unlike our Boston autumn.

Yet here each day the heat and light are intense, the sun blazes and scorches. It parches my garden and my skin; and though the frequent showers assuage the thirst of the plants, I feel no relief, for the blinding flashes of lightning and the ear-splitting crashes of thunder only grate further on my sorely tried spirit. During the winter the days are short, gloomy, and bitterly cold; now they are long, glaring, and oppressively hot. Tempers are short and hearts are heavy.

Only today a poor neighbor of mine, beset beyond endurance by the exhortations and denunciations of our ministers (although, to be fair, they did not single her out, but addressed us all), and despairing of ever attaining salvation, cast her infant daughter into a well and shrieked, "I am *certain* now that I am damned!" Then she collapsed, sobbing, "It is a comfort to be really certain of something, even though it be eternal damnation." To such straits have we been brought by our Christian leaders and the terrible heat, although such incidents—and there have been others—usually occur in the spring or autumn.

Fortunately one of Jane's great, useless, blundering boys was near at hand. He plunged into the well and racketed down on the bucket rope so quickly that the child was still breathing when hauled to the top. She is sleeping peacefully now in my cradle, while Anne comforts her mother, telling her that the Holy Ghost dwells in all those who love God and that if she loves God with all her heart, then she is bound to be saved. Poor tormented soul.

Feeling has been so high against the court concerning John Wheelwright's case that sentencing has been postponed in the hope that time will cool the hot tempers. In connection with John also, the court passed what is called an Alien law. This law prohibits strangers from remaining in Boston more than three weeks without the permission of a magistrate. Since John expects a boatload of friends shortly who might corrupt the colony with their "pernicious" views or, even worse, influence more people in John's behalf, the court desires to limit them in this way. The reason given, however, was that too many improvident strangers are making their way to Boston and becoming public charges. Of course, none of us wants to work hard and pay taxes to support some lazy fellow, but there are other ways of keeping people off the public rolls.

The governor's position is that the community and church have discretion to receive and reject. Harry objects strongly to this idea, saying that only Christ has such discretion. (He begins to sound much like Roger Williams.) Mr. Cotton was so outraged by the order that he declared he would move to Connecticut, but he was finally dissuaded from such drastic action. Harry and Will Coddington, however, refused to have anything more to do with the magistrates and moved over to the deacons' seats for church services. On Fast day, too, they did not worship here but went to Mt. Wollaston to be with John. It seems unbelievable that one cannot welcome one's own family and friends. And what of the strangers who have fled their English homes looking for religious tolerance in the New World, even as we did? They will not find it here. It all seems very strange to me.

Speaking of the court, Third month we had another election which threw everyone into turmoil and Harry into a perfect fury. Hoping to take advantage of the fact that many of Harry's friends were away fighting, and that many Boston men could not leave the city on election day, the old court majority voted to hold the election in New Towne. Of course Winthrop's cronies got him in as governor, defeating Harry; and Will Coddington lost as assistant. Then Coddington and Harry protested so loudly that the court hastily voided the votes and called for another election next day, in Boston. This time Mr. Coddington won but Harry lost again by a narrow margin. Naturally he and his supporters were bitterly disappointed.

Fourth month we had a day of thanksgiving to celebrate our war victories and other mercies, and to calm the people who had continued to grumble about the "election fraud," demanding that the incumbents be ousted. Also, John Davenport, another minister, arrived. There is really getting to be a surplus of them. As Mr. Cotton says, the only things plentiful and cheap in New England are milk and ministers!

Fifth month Lord Ley, who has been visiting the colony for several weeks—of course *he* does not count as an alien—was invited to the governor's house for dinner; and since he is Harry's guest, Harry had to be invited too.

But that young man, still bitterly disappointed over the election and the passage of the Alien law, not only declined the invitation but even refused to let his lordship go, and whisked him off to Nottle's Island to dine, in full view of the populace and to the public chagrin of the governor. It was really very rude of Harry, and the governor was furious; but as Harry's father is a wealthy knight, he dared not fuss about it. Poor Mr. Winthrop! He has been insulted in other ways too. After his reelection, the sergeants who served under Harry refused to continue under Winthrop, and he was forced to use his own servants to carry the halberds of office. Margaret takes it all very well, though, and we are still friends.

Then, only a few days ago, Lord Ley left for England and Harry went with him. He had applied for permission last winter under the press of family matters at home, but the court felt he ought not to leave at that time; now that he is no longer governor and his friends are in the minority, the court is glad to get rid of him. He has been a stalwart foe of intolerance in both theology and government, stoutly supporting Anne in her right to preach, and as vigorously opposing the Winthrop hierarchy.

I was very sorry to see him go for he was always cheerful, courageous, loyal, and friendly. He supped many times with us and was a source of endless amusement to me, for he would ascertain Will's opinions on some subject, then immediately take the opposite view and argue all evening in a very serious manner until Will began to lose his habitual calm and raise his voice. Then Harry, with a great shout of laughter, would clap him on the shoulder and cry, "You're quite right, my friend! I agree with you perfectly!" Will always looked confused and red for a moment, but soon gave in and chuckled over the joke, too.

Harry gave his hillside house to Mr. Cotton, whose hospitality he enjoyed upon arrival. To me he had already given many pleasant memories and much good advice. He was the older brother I had longed for, the younger one Will never had had. Alas, we have lost an able, intelligent representative and a very dear friend.

My Will has returned, this time to stay. He has promised me solemnly never to go to war again; even more, he has vowed to carry on Harry's fight for at least some freedom in religious and civil matters. He is indeed a changed man, to set himself against the governor and magistrates, all because of a few Indian savages whose cries still ring in his ears at night, and the smile of a little boy whose tiny hand clutches his great one trustfully. Soon there will be another child—perhaps a girl—to gladden our hearts.

[*Seventh month*]

The ministers of the colony have set Ninth day of this month as a time when they can all meet together at New Towne to discuss the theological differences which are prevalent among us. They call it a synod, the first ever held in the colony. I am extremely upset as it means, without a doubt, more trouble for Anne and John; they are the ones who have set the Boston church against all the others and the congregation against Winthrop and Wilson. If I were in Anne's place, I should be more discreet. Still, she feels she has a call to preach plainly and frankly, and does so fearlessly. May God protect them both!

[*Eighth month*]

The synod is over at last, after twenty-four days. Anne has been charged with eighty-two mistaken or blasphemous opinions, and with abuse of the Scriptures! I wonder the ministers didn't make it an even hundred while they were at it, or ninety-five, like Martin Luther. They claim she has used prophecy in her meetings, the meetings have been disorderly and without a scriptural basis, and they are therefore a nuisance. She has been ordered to appear before general court next month to answer the charges. Mr. Cotton, her idol, opposed the synod vigorously for a time, but finding the members adamant finally agreed.

Sixty of our leading citizens, Will among them, presented a petition to the synod respectfully urging that the charge of sedition against John be dropped (since no one had taken up arms following his sermon), and humbly promising to accept the decision if the petition were denied.

But the ministers were in no mood to be merciful and meek, and so the verdict of sedition and contempt, both civil charges, was affirmed by the religious body. Of course John had no chance under these circumstances.

Our own fat is in the fire! Will was questioned in meeting this afternoon about his part in the petition and his belief in the so-called antinomian doctrines. He spoke up stoutly, even rashly, saying that there is no inherent righteousness in Christians—one receives it only through grace—and that Adam was not made after God's image! I nearly fell off my bench at these words! If only I had been able to sit beside him, I could have nudged him sharply and perhaps prevented this outburst; but alas! we were far apart, and he was severely rebuked for his "monstrous opinion."

At last I am able to sit up for a while and take my writing desk on my knees, although I am still very weak. Both my body and brain are numb, and I can think of nothing but the sweet little girl we have lost.

Only ten days ago I felt wonderfully well, and so decided to stuff the boys' mattresses in the loft with fresh grass and stalks. I had completed my task and was starting down the stairs. Suddenly my shoe caught in my skirt and I felt myself tumbling, sprawling, thudding along each step. Later I heard whispers and recognized Anne and Jane hurrying about with serious faces. I fainted, floated back to consciousness, fainted again. At last Anne took my hand and murmured, "My dear, I am so sorry. The Lord giveth, and the Lord taketh away." She looked at me tenderly, then said, "It was a little girl."

I wept silently. Finally I asked, "May I see her?"

Anne shook her head. " 'Tis better not to." After a moment in which she struggled to control her own emotions, she added, "It was a very difficult birth. Even if she had lived . . ." She sighed heavily and went on. "No, sad as it is for thee to lose her, I know this way is best for all. Take heart, my dear, thou wilt have many more babies, believe me."

I looked at her with dull, tear-filled eyes, hardly seeing the sad, kind face; yet somehow I could see beyond the face and glimpse the spirit—strong, sure, and steadfast. She too had lost babies.

"I believe thee, Anne," I said at last and fell asleep while she stroked my hand with the gentle, capable fingers which have helped and comforted so many others.

That same evening Anne and Will trudged up the hill with our friends to the burying ground, the little casket on Will's shoulder, and solemnly interred our little girl. Upon Mr. Cotton's advice, the birth was not registered. He declared to Will that the hand of God was upon us, and that this would be a private lesson to us. How we have displeased God I do not know. Is it what Will said in the meeting? Is it because I am not so religious as Elizabeth Wilson and Sarah Cotton? Must I be punished because I truly can't believe what they believe? Or is Anne right in saying that it was not the hand of God at all which caused the accident; that it really was only my own clumsiness?

"If only I could be sure," I said to her.

"Be sure," she said quietly. "God loves thee, he would not hurt thee. Forget thy doubts and trust in him. It must have been for the best."

I do trust Anne, and I do want to believe that God is good and kind, but it is extremely hard to do so when nearly everyone else says just the opposite.

[*Ninth month*]

The outlook for our friends is bleak indeed. General Court today banished John Wheelwright for his Fast day sermon, and arbitrarily unseated Mr. Coggeshall and Mr. Aspinwall as Boston deputies for taking his part. Feeling against the court is so great that it has recessed and will travel to New Towne to hear the charges against Anne.

The first day of Anne's civil trial is over. Forty members of General Court gathered in the meetinghouse at New Towne this morning, filling the hard, backless benches and wearing thick hoods, caped coats, gloves, and jackboots, for the air is chilly and the meetinghouse unheated. Numerous spectators crowded in behind them, shoving and jostling for standing room. Governor Winthrop, magistrate and president of the court, took his place behind the table in the center of the platform. On either side, facing him, sat the other magistrates and deputies: Dudley, Endecott, and Coddington representing Boston, and the clergy: Wilson, Cotton, Welde, Peter, and others. Anne, looking pale yet resolute, and in the early months of another pregnancy, stood on the main floor slightly to the governor's left, facing him and the court. There were no specific charges, and no lawyers to speak for either side. Will Coddington has sent a few notes which I shall enlarge and post on the meetinghouse door in order that all of Anne's many friends may know how she fares.

Governor Winthrop began the proceedings in his usual calm, polite manner. "Mrs. Hutchinson, you have troubled the peace of the commonwealth and the churches here. You have uttered many things against our churches and ministers and continued to hold meetings in your house notwithstanding their condemnation by the general assembly as a thing not tolerable in the sight of God nor fitting for your sex. Therefore we have brought you here that you may plainly see your errors and repent; but if you do not, the court will see that you trouble us no longer."

"What is the charge, please, Governor?" said Anne.

"You helped get up the petition for Mr. Wheelwright."

"There is no law against this!"

"No, but you have broken the fifth commandment."

"What, must I ask permission of my parents before I can invite anyone to my house?"

"We do not speak of your natural parents, but of the rulers of this colony, who stand to you *in loco parentis*; and if your friends be of a different religion than that which we hold right, then you dishonor the rulers and deserve punishment."

"I accept no such premise!" she declared stoutly. "Nor do I think I have done anything to dishonor anyone."

"Come, come," he said testily, "tell us why you hold these meetings every week at your house."

"It is just as lawful for me to do so as for any of the rulers or ministers. Is there one standard for men and another for women? However, the reason was that I thought this would be an excellent opportunity for my sex to ask the questions which would otherwise go unasked."

"Now, Mrs. Hutchinson, this is very noble and selfless of you, no doubt, but we must have a scriptural basis for all our actions, you know. How can you justify this course with the Bible's teachings?"

"Why, I believe it is clearly stated in Titus that the older women may teach the younger ones."

"But what if a man should come? Ought you to instruct him?"

"I should think I might."

"By what right?"

"I have already stated the passage; and why should it not apply to any who seek help, rather than to women only?"

This was too much for the governor. "Enough!" he snapped. "Your views are not in accord with Scripture; you have also stirred up the people so that they no longer accept our decisions unquestioningly; and finally, we think it is not in the best interest of the colony for the ladies to be away from their home duties for such long periods of time—we have already set up enough meetings for them. Therefore we must order you to desist."

Anne replied coolly, "Do so—if you can find scriptural basis for it."

"Indeed!" exclaimed the governor. "We certainly can find scriptural basis for it, and for all our actions. We are the judges here," he said ominously, "and you shall soon discover what we can do."

Then Mr. Dudley unbridled his waspish tongue. "Ever since Mrs. Hutchinson arrived three years ago there has been naught but dissension in our colony. Away with her!" Thus did a childhood friend turn upon her!

The governor glared at this interruption, then resumed. "Did you ever say the ministers preached only a covenant of works?"

"Never!" said Anne indignantly.

"Well, is it truthful so to preach?"

"Certainly. However, this matter was not discussed in open meeting but in private conversation. I thought I was charged only with public utterances."

"Even though the matter was spoken about privately, it has now come to our attention and we must deal with it," Winthrop decided.

Pious Hugh Peter arose. "Mr. Wilson, Mr. Welde, and I

shall give you an honest account of what was said during the conversation. We do not like to inform against this lady, but of course we must consider what is best for the colony, not only at the present time, but also in the years to come."

Anne flushed with anger during his recital. When he had finished, she said hotly, "If Mr. Wilson will show the notes he took, you will see that Mr. Peter has not reported the facts correctly."

Mr. Peter bridled at this charge, but subsided as John Wilson spoke. "I am sorry to say, Mrs. Hutchinson," he simpered, "that I do not have the notes with me; anyway, I did not take complete notes."

The governor scowled at Wilson's slipshod methods and recessed the trial until the next morning.

When the court had reconvened, Anne requested permission to speak. "Let us end this wrangling once for all. If the ministers wish to accuse me, let them do it under oath!"

Amid the uproar that followed—put a minister under oath!—Endecott could be heard temporizing, "Now, now, let us not do anything hasty, something we might be sorry for. After all, we know these men very well indeed. I think we can trust them to tell the truth without an oath."

The governor put it up to the court. "Is there anyone opposed to dispensing with the oath?"

A whole chorus of voices replied; and, somewhat nettled at this turn of events, the governor called for the ministers to come forward.

"That is all very well," one of the deputies cried, "but is their testimony really valid? After all, Mrs. Hutchinson said these conversations took place in private; if this is so, they are privileged and cannot be introduced into court."

Little Dudley rushed in to worry the enemy. "Come, come! The court cannot be bothered with such silly questions. No witnesses have disproved the conversations."

"I have not been allowed to call any witnesses!" cried Anne in amazement.

John Coggeshall rose and said in his slow manner, "We think the elders ought to confer with Mr. Cotton about this before they testify, just to get all the facts straight."

"Indeed!" shrieked Endecott. "Do you think they don't know what was said without his help? What do you take them for? A pack of . . ." But he was pulled hastily to his seat by more prudent men and fell silent although continuing to glare fiercely at the assemblage.

"Mr. Coggeshall," said the governor sternly, "are you saying that the accused did not say the things that have been charged?"

"That is exactly what I am saying. I was there, I heard it all; and I say she certainly did not say everything they have reported."

"How dare you look at the court and say such things!" thundered Mr. Peter.

"Mr. Peter forbids me to speak, so I shall be silent," John pouted; and silent he remained. (Much help he was!)

"Well, Mr. Leverett, what have you to say?" inquired Winthrop as Thomas Leverett approached.

"As nearly as I can remember, she said that the other ministers did not preach the covenant of grace quite as clearly or strongly as Mr. Cotton did."

The governor sighed. There was no help for it now. "Come forward and testify, Mr. Cotton," he said.

John Cotton strutted importantly to the front of the platform. He gazed calmly at Anne as if to say, "Don't worry, my dear, everything will be all right now that I'm here." She responded with a warm smile.

"I really did not expect to be called," the minister said,

"so I did not attempt to refresh my memory." (Not expect to be called? Anne's idol, friend, mentor?) "However, I do seem to recall that the conversation took a rather unfortunate turn, and that they asked her how she thought their preaching differed from mine. Of course, I always feel 'tis better not to make comparisons, especially . . ."

"Yes, yes," said the governor. "We know how you dislike comparisons. Just get on with the facts, please."

"Well, she said they did not preach the covenant of grace and the seal of the spirit as I did. It was not said in any derogatory way, you understand, nor discussed further, and my colleagues did not appear to take any offense at that time. Mrs. Hutchinson did not mention the covenant of works at all, nor accuse them of living under it."

At this flat statement, Cotton preened himself while the court whispered among one another, for this totally refuted the ministers' claims.

"If I may speak for a moment," said Anne impatiently, "perhaps I can explain how all this came about. Disturbed at the popish ceremonies and doctrines prevalent in our English churches, I decided to spend a day in prayer and fasting, hoping thus to gain some insight into the best means of correcting these evils. As I read the Bible, my eyes fell upon the words, 'And every spirit that confesseth not that Jesus Christ is come in the flesh is not of God: and this is that spirit of antichrist. . . .' I pondered this for some time. Were the papists antichrists? The nonconformists? The Turks? I could not decide. Then I saw this passage: 'He that believeth on the Son of God hath the witness in himself: he that believeth not God hath made him a liar. . . .' At once it was clear to me that antichrist was anyone who did not preach the ways and doctrines of the New Testament but clung to the Old.

"I know in my heart that this is the truth. If you wish to

condemn me for this, I can only say, 'The Lord's will be done.' "

"Mrs. Hutchinson, what made you think this was the correct interpretation of the text?"

"How did Abraham know that it was God commanding him to sacrifice his son?"

"He heard God's voice," said Dudley.

"So was this revealed to me."

"What!" shouted Dudley. "A revelation!"

"Aye, by the voice of his own Spirit to my soul!"

The court broke into a great uproar. Mr. Cotton's jaw dropped, and he gazed foolishly about as did the rest of Anne's friends. Revelation! Everyone knew that all truth for all time to come was contained in the Bible, and that no further revelations could be made. The case was certainly hopeless now.

With difficulty Winthrop called the court to order. Anne was pale but undaunted. "Mind what you do!" she cried. "I am in the hands of the eternal Jehovah!"

"Do you think to be delivered from our verdict—and sentence—by a miracle, like Daniel?" asked the governor incredulously.

"I look for the Lord to deliver me by his providence," she replied.

"If the court please," sneered Endecott, "I have heard some rumors of these revelations before, but to have them announced in open court as fact is most shocking. Perhaps Mrs. Hutchinson's great friend and teacher, Mr. Cotton, would care to enlighten us as to his views on the matter."

Mr. Cotton proceeded to do so with many erudite expressions and cautious circumlocutions.

Then, after considerable wrangling, Will Coddington, who had been silent all this time, arose and began to speak in his precise, deliberate fashion. "If the court please, I have some knowledge of the law, as have you, Governor, and several others here; and it seems to me we have all forgotten that we are not permitted to be both accuser and judge. We must be one or the other." (From the surprised expressions, this had evidently not occurred to anyone else.) "Furthermore," he went on, "we all know that the Holy Spirit *does* speak through occasional human beings. This happened frequently while the apostles lived, has happened since then, and can happen today."

"All right!" the governor snapped. "Suppose we forget about the things she said out of court. What she has said here today would still be grounds for strong action."

"I protest!" shouted Coddington, always short-tempered when crossed in any way. "These proceedings are quite illegal, the charges are unfounded and unproved, and justice is not to be had here! This woman has broken no law, civil or moral!"

"Come, come," said Dudley fussily, clasping his plump stomach, "shall we stay here all day and starve?"

"Well, I am against banishing her," said one.

" 'Tis only what she deserves," said another.

"She has not been convicted by sworn witnesses," said others, "but it is getting late, and we can't be too careful about keeping down dangerous views like these, so we had better go ahead and put her out of the colony anyway; then we shall have some peace again."

"But these views were expressed in private, gentlemen!" Coddington had not given up. "You cannot try her on private conversations. Indeed, if anyone is to be tried, it should be these men who have betrayed her confidence. They are the ones who have broken the moral law!"

"Why don't you swear the witnesses, Governor?" cried one. "Don't *you* trust them either?"

"Well, well," he replied testily. "Let them be sworn then. Any elder will do."

At the conclusion of their testimony Winthrop expressed his views. "The court is convinced that Mrs. Hutchinson's views are both erroneous and dangerous. We cannot permit her to continue preaching them. Therefore if you agree that she ought to be imprisoned until such time as she can be permanently banished from the colony, hold up your right hand." All but three so voted.

"Contrary-minded?" Coddington and Mr. Colborn held up theirs.

Deputy Jennison, shaking his head, declared, "I can't decide one way or the other."

Winthrop ignored him and turned to Anne. "Mrs. Hutchinson, the sentence of the court is that you shall be banished from our colony."

Anne was undaunted. "I desire to know why I am banished," she demanded.

In a sudden fury, Winthrop retorted, "Say no more! The court knows why and is satisfied."

And so the civil trial is over. Now Anne must remain a prisoner until spring, when she will be tried by the church. She is to stay in Roxbury with Mr. Welde's brother Joseph and his family, far from her own family and friends who might be "contaminated and seduced" by her "frightful" doctrines and character. I feel dreadfully bitter about it all, but Will says her true friends will remain faithful. "Besides," he grinned, "Anne is still confident that a providential hand will snatch her from the brink of disaster."

As if the court had not already done enough mischief this term, it has certainly accomplished its full share, and more, today with the decree that forty of the antinomian petition signers be disarmed immediately "as likely, through revelations, to attack those who differed" from them! Twenty other signers have recanted and been forgiven. Aspinwall, Coggeshall, Captain Underhill, and Will have been disarmed and disfranchised, and Aspinwall banished for his part in the petition. He maintained in court that it is lawful for subjects to petition; while the court objected that 'twas not a petition but a seditious libel. Upon Aspinwall's demanding the scriptural reference for banishment, Mr. Winthrop replied that it was ordered in Genesis 21, when Sarah prevailed upon Abraham to cast out Hagar and Ishmael, because Ishmael was not the chosen heir.

Thus the colonies are the chosen heirs of Abraham in the New World, and those of us who disagree with our spiritual leaders—who are in league with the civil authorities—must stifle our objections or be cast into the wilderness. Will Coddington, for defending Anne, is "permitted" to leave the colony within three months (in the midst of winter) with nine of his most ardent followers; the only reason he was not banished is that he has considerably more money and influence in England than Mr. Aspinwall.

To such a pass matters have come that a man must give up his arms, his only means of defense, because he seeks mercy for a friend. It is finally quite clear to me: The minsters in their meetinghouses are more savage than the ravening wolves which prowl our streets, and more relentless than the cruel and wily redskins skulking in the forests. God grant that I may never stand before them!

John Wheelwright fled the colony early this morning before daybreak. His two weeks' grace period at an end, he had to leave at once or face imprisonment or worse. The weather is very cold, with a heavy snow falling, but Will saw him on his way with a horse and sackful of provisions. I pray that he will reach his friends in the North safely.

John Clarke, the physician, and two others are also abroad in the storm, secretly searching for a suitable location for those of us who are compelled by decree or conscience to leave our homes. The Coddingtons, Hutchinsons, Coggeshalls, and Aspinwalls are going, and Will is determined to go, too.

"No man is going to take my gun away from me!" he raved. "A man has to have something to protect himself with! Why, next they'll take my shop and mill on some even flimsier pretext!"

Of course he is right, but it will be dreadful to leave our comfortable home, our profitable mill, and all our many friends to start again in some strange, unsettled place. I wish we could return to England, home, and Mother—but Will would never hear of it.

[*Tenth month*]

At my insistence Will rode with me to Roxbury today in an attempt to see Anne. The stormy weather has abated temporarily and there is only an inch or two of soft snow on the ground, so I felt we must make the effort. Muffled in cloak and scarf, I huddled behind him on the horse, clinging tightly for both safety and warmth.

We had no difficulty finding the house as it is a large one directly opposite Thomas Welde's own—his brother is quite well-to-do. However, Will thought it wise to ride on past and come up at the back, reasoning that they would never permit Anne to occupy a room on the street where she might so easily pervert passersby with a glimpse of her face through a tiny window. He was right. Dismounting in the orchard, we tied the horse and crept to the few rear windows. We glanced quickly into each until through one we spied Anne sitting on a stool in a little dark room, reading her Bible.

Tapping lightly on the pane, we saw her look up in curiosity, then amazement. Her sweet, serious face lighted up with a broad smile as she recognized us, and hurrying over, she threw open the window. I embraced her tearfully while Will sauntered off to keep a lookout.

"How art thou, Anne?" I sobbed, the great tears flooding my eyes. "Is it so terrible? Are they kind? Do they feed thee enough?"

"What a goose thou art, Mary!" she exclaimed fondly, "weeping over an unregenerate sinner like me! But 'tis wonderful to see a friendly face again. Tell me, what news of my family?"

I then told her what little news there was. Her family, although desperately lonely for her, was well provided for. The married girls saw to the cooking and the others cared for the younger children and did the cleaning. Her husband was watched closely lest he try to communicate with her, but he sent his love and urged her not to despair.

Her face saddened as she thought of the distant family who had lived so happily and warmly in her heart, and she sighed. "Ah, Mary, 'twill be a long, hard winter without any little ones running to me for comfort, or nose-wiping, or story-telling. The only voices I hear now are the smug, hard, nasal voices of the ministers who visit me daily, urging me to repent and recant. I am not allowed even to speak with Mrs. Welde or any other woman, and my only reading is the Bible. But that is a great consolation to me and I am confident I shall survive the solitude and the catechizing."

"Hast thou need for anything?" I asked as Will approached.

"Nothing," she replied, "except the assurance that I am not forgotten."

"That thou art not! Indeed, our friends are even now seeking a place where we may all gather to live as we choose when thou art free again and . . ."

Here I was interrupted by a crash as the door to Anne's room was flung open.

"Ah!" cried Thomas Welde, striding into the room. "What have we here? Another of your contentious, seditious antinomians? Take care, Mrs. Dyer," he growled, "lest you pull down upon your own head the righteous wrath of God and his just punishment. You too can be expelled from our midst, like any other vile serpent!"

His vicious words thundered in my ears and I shrank back.

"Ho, there!" he shouted to a servant. "Bring some boards and close up this window! I'll put a stop to this meddlesome preaching, you viper, you spawn of Satan, you . . . "

"God be with thee, Anne!" I whispered. "Forgive me for adding to thy burdens."

"Hush!" she smiled. "Thy visit hath done me more good than harm in easing my worried mind. Be off now, and pray for me!"

"I will! I will!" I promised fervently, and as we stumbled away I could see Anne smiling sweetly at her gaoler and giving back in a quiet, ladylike yet effective manner, with no doubt a scriptural basis, as good as he gave.

[*Twelfth month*]

A message from John Wheelwright reports he is safe and well in New Hampshire and hopes to found his own village in the spring. At present, he writes, the weather is so intensely cold that if he had ever had any seditious or contemptuous feelings, they were certainly frozen hard now. Would that our own Winthrop, Wilson, and Welde might visit the northern region and thus return with cooler, saner heads!

John Clarke and party have returned, not finding a suitable location, and will go out again when the weather moderates.

I fear Jane is not well. She has always been extremely fond of Anne, helping with the children or the sick whenever I could not go, and trying to emulate Anne's successful cures with her own superstitious amulets and charms—as if anyone could become pregnant through crushing mandrake roots! But Jane insists they are effective and visits all the barren women secretly with her silly oils.

For a cough, she advises the patient to put one of her hairs between two slices of bread and feed it to the dog; the dog will then receive the cough. For thrush, Dr. Jane holds a frog's head inside the baby's mouth for a few seconds; this passes the disease on to the frog, of course. I know of this because I caught her doing it to Sam. And for warts, one can not only rid oneself of them, but foist them off on someone else by touching the wart with a small stone, wrapping the stone in an ivy leaf, and then casting it into the street; whoever picks up the stone will promptly sprout a wart—although why anyone would pick up anything, even gold, let alone a stone, from these filthy streets with their slops, garbage, excrement, and mud is more than I can fathom.

I warned Jane there would be trouble if she didn't stop this nonsense, but she persists, and the shocking thing is that so many women believe her. Now that Anne is a prisoner, Jane goes about muttering to herself much of the time and glaring suspiciously at me. I believe she thinks I am responsible in some way.

To make matters worse Margaret Winthrop confided that Major Scott is spreading scandalous rumors about some alleged misbehavior on Anne's and my part with Harry Vane on the voyage to Boston! Everyone knows Anne came over first, and that there was no possible opportunity for anything like that aboard ship, even if one were not sick the whole time. However, there are always gullible, unthinking creatures who delight in snapping up such malicious gossip and adding to it as they pass it along.

Oh, dear, this has been a frightful winter, gloomy, dark, cold, wet, and stultifying as usual, but with the added burden on our hearts and minds of the injustices and cruelties perpetrated here in the name of religion.

1638

[*First month*]

Anne's church trial began this afternoon in the midst of a late snowstorm. Drummed to meeting at eight o'clock we endured the morning sermon and prayers, alternately yearning for and dreading the start of the trial after lunch.

If only Will and her other advocates were here to sustain her at this critical time! But John Clarke summoned them quietly a few days ago to meet with the Narragansett chief concerning the sale of some of his land for our new settlement, and they have not yet returned. Even Will Hutchinson is gone. I believe their absence has caused the governor and Mr. Wilson to arrange the trial for this particular time. Oh, those villains!

Anne looked quite ill: The solitude, inactivity, and incessant badgering of the ministers has had its effect on her health. Her spirit remained indomitable, however, for she smiled faintly when I caught her eye. I was barely able to smile in return, so great were my apprehension and sympathy.

Mr. Wilson, on the other hand, was in excellent health

and spirits. With his shriveled features and cold cod-eyes, his black skullcap and black gown, he looked for all the world like a hungry vulture about to swoop down on its prey. He spoke first, asking that all the day's proceedings be conducted in a spirit of love. (From almost anyone else I could accept the sentiment wholeheartedly, but it was quite ridiculous coming from him.)

John Cotton then assumed charge and nodded for Mr. Leverett to read the list of errors. Then Mr. Welde and Mr. Eliot had charges to make, and so he read those.

"What say you, Mrs. Hutchinson?"

Anne replied in a firm voice. "If these beliefs are in error, I ought to renounce them. But if I may I should like first to ask by which of the Lord's commandments do these elders, speaking to me in private here and in Roxbury, now publicize these things before the church? How can they charge me with opinions expressed in prison? I think it very wrong of them."

Mr. Shepard said somewhat defiantly, "Not understanding some of her remarks at the court trial, I went to see her privately at Brother Welde's house to argue with her. When she remained adamant, I knew there was no other course but to charge her publicly. It was the only way she might be persuaded to renounce these heresies!"

The congregation began to discuss this with some heat among one another. Suddenly Anne staggered, and only just caught herself from falling. Mr. Cotton ordered a stool brought for her, and she smiled gratefully at him. But when two of her sons attempted to plead in her behalf, he set upon them as mercilessly as the other ministers.

At last pious old Oliver quavered, "Since the early churches acted as one man, let us lay these two brethren under an admonition with their mother, that we may proceed without opposition."

Wilson smiled thinly, rubbing his hands in anticipation. No one dared say a word. All rustling and coughing ceased. "Very well," he said. "With the consent—the silent consent—of the church, we shall proceed with the admonition. Mr. Cotton?"

What cowardice, what betrayal of friendship! To clear himself of any taint from his close association with Anne this friend, this teacher, this idol for whom she left safety, comfort, position, home, and country, whom she followed into the dangers and discomforts of the New World, this pompous paragon, this cowardly cleric was now to pronounce the censure of the church upon her! It was intolerable, I could not bear it. Anne herself was dreadfully pale.

"I confess," he said, not looking at Anne, "I have not been ready to believe reports, and have been slow to proceed, for lack of testimony. But now that each witness has spoken and the truth been affirmed, it would be our sin if we should not join in the same. And I admonish you, her sons, to desist from comforting and supporting her in her errors and thus keeping her from repentance, but instead attempt to bring her to knowledge of her wrong ways. As for the sisters here, I doubt not you have received much good and help from conversing with her, but I admonish you now, let not the good you have received from her make you to receive all for good that comes from her. If you have received good, keep it carefully. But if you have drunk in with this good any evil or poison, make speed to vomit it up again and repent of it, and do not harden her in her errors by pitying her or confirming her opinions, but pray faithfully for her soul." (He glanced sharply at me.)

"And now, Sister,"—he paused while Anne rose and faced him—"it is true that since your coming here you have been an instrument of doing good to many. Notwithstanding we have a few things against you, some of a weighty and dangerous nature."

"I still maintain I did not believe any of these things before my imprisonment, and you have no right to charge me with them," said Anne, in a clear voice which reached even Mr. Oliver's deaf ear.

Cotton ignored the interruption and went on. "And so I do admonish you and charge you in the name of Christ Jesus and in the name of the church, that you sadly consider the great hurt you have done to the church, the great dishonor you have brought to Jesus Christ, and the evil you have done to many a poor fool, and beg him for repentance. And so the Lord carry home to your soul what I have spoken to you in his name."

So saying he retreated a step, and Mr. Wilson closed the inquisition. "The congregation will assemble this day sevennight to hear further charges against this woman."

Thus ended the first day. Anne was hustled off to Mr. Wilson's house, her new prison, not even permitted to hug her babies or clasp the hand of a friend.

Jane is worse than ever. She is no help at all around the house, always sneaking out when I need her most. Heaven knows where she goes or what she does; she will barely speak to me, let alone confide in me. She seems to blame me in some way for Anne's misfortunes.

The men have not returned.

[*Second month, Lecture day*]

After another sermon and midday meal we gathered again in meetinghouse. Anne looked very grave, yet there was no fear in her sad eyes, only pity for her tormentors.

All the other churches were there, and dozens of people from miles away, in addition to our own congregation, were crowding and pressing for benches and standing room. As a prosperous member of the Boston church I was able to take my accustomed place near the front. I tried to smile at Anne, but the tears started to my eyes. How brave she was, facing the elders like a gentle doe encircled by vicious, snapping hounds!

The trial resumed with some conciliatory words by Mr. Cotton which served only to inflame Anne's accusers.

"I say that her disrespect toward the magistrates was a great sin," cried Wilson, "but even greater was her derogatory preaching of God's appointed ministers so that she could set herself above them!" (Are we really getting to the crux of the matter now? Is it really pique rather than doctrine which moves these men to such drastic action?)

Hugh Peter had a pearl of wisdom to deliver to Anne. "And I say you have stepped out of your place; you have rather been a husband than a wife, and a preacher than a hearer, and a magistrate than a subject!"

Wilson could not restrain himself. "I look at her as a dangerous instrument of the devil, full of schismatical and foul falsehoods and lies. Let the church express themselves whether she should not be separated from the congregation of the Lord!"

"Aye," said Cotton, "we received her into the church; we must now thrust her out."

Then up rose Nicholas Easton, one of our few remaining friends. "The Bible says, 'He that confesseth and forsaketh sin shall have mercy.' On what grounds then can we excommunicate this poor, harassed woman?"

"Let us wait a little longer. Perhaps she will yet reconsider," said Richard Scott (the one who had married Anne's sister Catharine).

Alarmed at the support shown for Anne, Shepard plunged in quickly. "I see it is the will of many here to coddle this viper by only admonishing her a second time. Is this the way to honor God, by nurturing those who reject his truth and affront decent folk with their foul blasphemies and devil-inspired heresies? I say, to show mercy to such as she is to sin ourselves and lay ourselves open to eternal damnation!"

Wilson sprang forward. "We must proceed!"

The other ministers rose as if by prearrangement. Wilson motioned to Anne. She also rose but appeared dazed at this sudden turn of events. The congregation, seeing the ministers standing, straggled to its feet, although there were many who still did not realize what was happening.

"Therefore," intoned Wilson in his most nasal and ominous tones, "forasmuch as you, Mrs. Hutchinson, have highly transgressed and offended, therefore, in the name of our Lord Jesus Christ and in the name of the church, I do not only pronounce you worthy to be cast out, but I *do* cast you out and in the name of the church I do deliver you up to Satan, that you may learn no more to blaspheme, to seduce, and to lie, and I do account you from this time forth to be a heathen and a publican and so to be held of all the brethren and sisters of this congregation and of others. Therefore, I command you in the name of Christ Jesus and of this church, as a leper to withdraw yourself out of the congregation. As formerly you have despised and condemned the holy ordinances of God and turned your back on them, so you may now have no part in them nor benefit by them!"

He and the other ministers triumphantly turned their backs to her. She paused a moment, looking rather astonished at this suddenly wrought catastrophe, but still hopeful. Then, realizing that despite her faith the Lord was not going to deliver her but that she must bear this cross herself, she started down the aisle.

Many were the sad and tear-stained faces which, as she approached, turned away in obedience not to their own desire but to that of their priests. There was not a movement, not a sound except for a stifled sob here and there. As the enormity of her plight pressed about her, she faltered and seemed about to faint.

Suddenly I could bear it no longer. My heart bursting with love and anguish, I stepped to Anne's side, slipped my arm about her waist and walked with her from meeting, glaring defiantly at the few who met my eye.

The wrath of the magistrates has fallen upon us with a vengeance. Today the general court forbade Jane to meddle further in medical matters except with the express consent of the elders, upon pain of expulsion, or worse, as a witch. Poor, simple Jane! Of course her silly notions are partly responsible, but I fear this is retaliation and an indirect warning by the court for the times when Will and I have taken Anne's part.

Jane has been weeping all day. When she heard the news, she rushed into the house and flung herself at my feet, begging me to save her and confessing all the vile rumors she has spread of late about me and my poor innocent babe. Anne would not let her look at the little thing when 'twas born; and in her spite toward me she has whispered that the child was a monster, with scales and claws and horns, the product of an evil mind and body.

Heartsick as I am at this latest news, there can no longer be any doubt as to our future course: When Anne leaves, as she must very soon, we shall go with her never to return. Where decent, kindhearted folk may be maligned and mistreated for the promptings of their conscience, and where evil machinations are cloaked in the guise of religious fervor, there is not the place for such independent and stubborn spirits as the Dyers. And though the wilderness be wide and strange, though pestilence overwhelm and decimate our band, or searing torch and rending fang attack and maim us from the wood, yea, despite these dangerous and uncertain prospects, we go forth gladly for the honor and glory of Almighty God, the Eternal and Everlasting Father, who watches over us all, even the sparrows. Praised be his holy name!

The men have returned, having traded with the Narragansetts for Aquiday Island, near Roger Williams' Providence Plantations. Anne, Jane—we could not leave her behind even after her terrible slander—Will and I with our children depart tomorrow by boat, to foil any pursuers; for the court is preparing to arrest Anne for overstaying her leave. We shall rest at Anne's Mt. Wollaston farm for a few days, then go overland to Aquiday; the others will follow shortly. Thus ends our brief stay in the Bay Colony. The milk and honey of the Promised Land has turned to bitter vetch in our mouths and the shining promise in our hearts to ugly dross. But steadfast hope and faith we have still, and resolute determination yet to harvest all our crop of longings and of dreams.

We leave at dawn.

Pocasset

[*Fourth month*] *Aquiday Island*

The sun streams down warmly, and a gentle summer breeze slips across the grassy meadows fragrant with wild roses. A few clean fat clouds drift across the bluest of skies. My mountainous wash is spread out on bushes to dry and whiten in the sun, while little Sam chases butterflies and explores each vivid blossom that nods and beckons in the breeze. Close by I hear the clack of the loom brought forward to the entrance of a cave, the lighthearted chatter of the women as they saunter to the brook with buckets, and the sharp, vigorous cries of an infant clamoring for his lunch. In the distance some of the men are plowing and sowing, while nearby carpenters fill the air with the thud of their hammers and the rasp of their saws from dawn to dusk. Every week brings new families to our tiny settlement and all must be housed before winter. The caves are a source of endless delight to the children but we women long for something less gloomy and inconvenient. Everything is tied in bundles and I for one can seldom find what I want until long after the need for it has ceased.

Still, we are so fortunate to be here at all that I should not complain. It was only because of their friendship for Roger Williams that Canonicus and Miantonomo sold us this property at all, as the Narragansetts are jealous of their land. This island, in addition to grass rights on the other islands, cost us forty fathoms of white wampum, and ten coats and twenty hoes. These wampum beads are made from the inside of certain shells and derive their value from the color of the shell and the length of time necessary to carve the beads. Since one fathom is worth five or ten shillings, this means we paid the equivalent of only twenty English pounds, surely a most advantageous purchase on our part. Morever, not only was the white wampum less expensive than the purple or black, it also implies the Indians' good wishes for our health, peace, and riches.

How clean and peaceful it all seems here! Yet the news brought us by recent arrivals from Boston is such that it besmirches the very atmosphere and reminds us again of the malignant spirits still hounding us relentlessly from afar.

Those wicked, inhuman fiends, Governor Winthrop among them, acting on Jane's irresponsible gossip, have exhumed my sweet baby and solemnly proclaimed to the church that her "horns, scales, and claws" were a judgment of God, and that Anne's "monstrous" miscarriage shortly after our arrival here signifies, according to her former friend, John Cotton, her error in denying inherent righteousness. Thomas Welde—or Warden Welde, as we call him—is reported to have declared that Anne brought forth thirty monstrous births, one for each of her "erroneous" opinions. I am glad to see they have reduced the number from the original eighty-two. If we wait long enough, they may decide they were not erroneous after all.

Of course this is just more of their sanctimonious nonsense, for intelligent people know such births are not possible; and besides, Will and Anne know my little girl was not born so, while I myself assisted John Clarke, our respected teacher and physician, when he attended Anne. I do not understand why John Winthrop should join in such calumny, but then, I suppose he has no choice. If he wishes to remain in power, he must not antagonize the priests.

Despite these nauseous slanders and her own personal misfortunes, Anne has recovered her cheerful spirits and resumed her good works and preaching with even greater zeal. Of her excommunication she declares, " 'Twas the greatest happiness, next to Christ, that ever befell me." She says this does not mean she was happy to be cast out of the church, but that she was happy to serve the Lord and witness to his truth as she understands it.

When I wondered about this, she quoted Scripture

saying, " 'And who is he that will harm you if ye be followers of that which is good? But and if ye suffer for righteousness' sake, happy are ye: and be not afraid . . . neither be troubled. . . . For it is better, if the will of God be so, that ye suffer for well doing, than for evil doing. . . .' "

What a marvellous example she has been to me—patient, kind, gentle, yet courageously outspoken when the need arises. I hope my life may be as useful and as brave.

The men have drawn up a form of government already and elected officers. Our compact provides that all laws and ordinances be passed in town meeting by a majority of householders, and that no new settler be admitted except by majority consent. Will said this did not sound much like liberty to him, but the others assured him it was just to keep out intolerant people and troublemakers. Will Coddington is our first magistrate and henceforth to be called "judge." Thomas Aspinwall is our secretary, and Will Dyer our extremely intelligent and efficient clerk.

[*Seventh month*]

The news from Boston is that the court, after deliberating profoundly and at length, has chosen a name for the college. It will be called "Harvard College," because of the books and money willed the institution by John Harvard, a former young minister at Charlestown. College indeed! 'Tis only a house stuck in the middle of a pasture, with more cows in attendance than students. Both the students and the master, Nathaniel Eaton, live and work there. People say that Mrs. Eaton starves the boys and that Nathaniel beats them, and that the boys probably learn more about hickory and hunger than about Hebrew and Greek. Still, I suppose 'tis better than nothing.

We hear that Roger Williams is still rather unsettled in

his religious beliefs—now the Established Church, now the Baptists, now the Seekers. Hearing of all this, Mr. Coddington remarked to Will, "Pshaw! The man is a mere weathercock, constant only in his unconstancy."

But after all, Mr. Williams established the principle of religious liberty for all his settlers, and there is no reason he should not make full use of it himself.

We have all been glad to hear that Miantonomo and Uncas, enemies for many years, have signed a treaty agreeing to confer with English emissaries on all their disputes. This will not only decrease the Indian raids against each other, but also enable us to keep informed on their other activities, and prevent the Dutch from gaining any undue advantage over us.

John Davenport, who acquitted himself at Anne's trial somewhat better than some other ministers I could mention, and Theophilus Eaton, a merchant, have led a group of wealthy persons to the Connecticut Valley and called their settlement "New Haven." The government is theocratic, of course, and the laws very strict. These ordinances prohibit observing Christmas and Saints' days, playing cards, making mince pies, reading Common Prayer, or playing musical instruments except trumpet, drum, and jewsharp. Men must not wear wigs or long hair but cut their locks to conform to round caps, and all married persons must live together, even if they are dreadfully unhappy and unable to get along. Many of these prohibitions and stipulations were enforced in Boston, too, and it is sad to see this rigid control extended to another colony.

[*Eighth month*]

Providence has now added more property to its holdings to be used as an asylum for religious and political freedom seekers, and for an Indian mission. Since Mr. Williams has always treated them courteously and fairly and even learned their language, old Chief Canonicus and younger Miantonomo have responded in similar fashion and now show their respect and friendship for Mr. Williams at every opportunity. Their people also are beginning to respond to his religious teachings, and so he has set up the first mission to the Indians.

The town itself begins now to look more like an English settlement. Unlike Rome, it is built on only three hills, and faces the long, narrow, island-studded waters of Narragansett Bay. The wigwams have been replaced by oak houses on stone foundations laid neatly along the main street which follows the Great Salt River for two miles. Right behind the houses are vegetable gardens, barns, and other outbuildings for cattle and horses and tools; then the orchard with its sweet scent of apples, peaches, pears, berries, and its steady hum of honey-bearing bees; and at its foot the family burying ground, vacant now but soon to gather multitudes of hapless tenants into its mansions.

As for Providence government matters, they are changing too. While at first there was no organized government, the settlers did act to provide that "no man should be molested for his conscience" by either the magistrates or the church. Having suffered such molestations themselves in Boston, they were determined to prevent its recurrence here. The families used to meet every fortnight to consult about common problems and decide them by mutual consent. The bachelors however, not being entitled to vote, were discontented and asked for majority rule, and Mr. Williams complied. His plan made no provision for executive officers or constables. Instead, everything was to be improvised when the need arose, and dispensed with when the need was over in order to avoid jealousies arising from delegated power.

Here in Pocasset everyone continues to be busy, the men harvesting, the women preparing warm clothing and storing the garden produce for winter's use. Nicholas Easton's sawmill has furnished us a plenty of lumber so that all of us are housed comfortably. Now he can concentrate his energies on building ships to carry on the promising trade in furs and naval stores. This entire country is really remarkable, miles upon miles of dense forests all up and down the coast and far into the interior, they tell me. One seldom sees anything like it in England except in the wildest, most remote parts. Even Sherwood Forest is but a park compared with these extravagant stands. And of course the woods are teeming with fur-bearing animals just waiting to be trapped.

[*Eleventh month*]

A severe wind and rain storm of several days' duration early this month has caused some damage to our buildings and torn up many trees. Some of our supplies were carried away and food is very short among our ninety-one families. Water stands twenty(!) feet deep in the Connecticut meadows, and travelers from Boston report that the damage there is extensive, that fences and houses are destroyed. Earth shocks were felt over a large area one day. Here we were all at prayer at Anne's house, it being Lecture day and hers the largest house. The building shook horribly for several long moments and we were all terrified, all except Anne. " 'Tis the Holy Ghost come down upon us as he did upon the apostles!" she declared solemnly. Will was skeptical about this explanation later at home, but nothing seems strange to me anymore. We all know God manifests himself in natural phenomena at times.

Quarterly meeting this month decided to enlarge the governing body to three elders who will assist the judge. They are to govern according to "the general rule of the word of God or by direction of a majority." The meeting has power to review all action of the judge and elders and to repeal whatever it considers unjust or unwise.

Judge Coddington was vastly displeased at this curbing of his theocratic autocracy in favor of a trend toward democracy. He thinks people are socially unequal and that there ought to be class distinctions, and "that each person may best serve God by remaining in that station to which he was divinely appointed," one of his favorite quotations from John Cotton, that paragon of wisdom, courage, and loyalty whom he likes much better now that they are no longer competing for power. He likes to conclude with a word from his old friend Winthrop: "Democracy is always of least continuance and fullest of trouble, whereas the elected magistrates and governor are stewards of God."

These opinions are just what one expects from such men who are wealthy, educated, and born to positions of influence and power. 'Tis no wonder they blanch when a common, though educated, tanner like Nicholas Easton declares on Lecture day that each of the elect has both Holy Ghost and Devil dwelling within his soul. Naturally, then, each is as qualified as the next to speak on religious matters, and from there it is only a step to political and social equality. Mr. Herne, on the other hand, is trying to make the position for women even lower than it is now by saying they have no souls. But this notion has not gained much headway—we women see to that!

Samuel Gorton, a clothier and sometime preacher, is

another one who must put in his tuppence' worth. Arriving in Boston during the Wheelwright trial, he could not stomach the restrictions put upon religious thought and moved to Plymouth, where sermons are not so long and heads are usually somewhat cooler. However, his servingmaid was caught smiling in church one sabbath and brought trembling before the magistrates. Unmindful of Mr. Gorton's doubtlessly stirring and eloquent defense, the court found her guilty and levied a small fine. Mr. G. was outraged and was so imprudent as to express his contempt for the magistrates. For this insubordination he was promptly banished from the colony. Thence he made his way here with his family and maid in knee-deep snow and is now antagonizing everyone by declaring that this government is not valid because we hold no royal patent and do not exercise our authority according to English common law. Will thinks there may be something to his point about the patent, but we shall have to wait and see. Mr. G. likes to refer to himself as the "professor of the mysteries of Christ," but Will refers to him as a troublemaker and a candidate for Bedlam.

Thus our little colony is in violent upheaval. The prosperous and peaceful days of summer have given way to winter's hunger and dissension. But spring will come again with all her hope and promise, and while we commit our lives to God and follow where he leads, we cannot fail to find peace and plenty.

1639-1640

[*First month, 1639*]

Another new year, another move. Will says he is tired of all the bickering about religion and politics and is ready to go with Judge Coddington and settle elsewhere. The judge is irked at not having more power. Others also are disappointed at the controversies which have arisen.

I protested of course. "Why not stay and try to bring some order into this chaos instead of running away?"

"Because, my dear," Will replied, "these opinions are too diverse to allow of any reconciliation. Some desire political and religious autonomy, some are still tied to English ways; some wish to follow this teacher, some wish to follow that one. Tempers have already flared, and I fear for another antinomian disaster unless we separate peaceably now while we have the opportunity. None of us is a fanatic," he concluded, "but we all have invested much of our money and lives in this venture, too much to risk for a few radical, untested ideas when our experience and natural conservatism indicate a safer, wiser direction."

So Anne and I must part. How I shall miss her friendship, her warm heart and witty tongue! The Boston church this month sent a committee of three to demand of us in Pocasset why we allow Anne to live and worship with us in defiance of the excommunication order. She parried all their remarks in her usual high-spirited manner, citing biblical authority for her "heretical" views.

And her husband William! Usually quiet and seemingly meek, he can nevertheless assert himself vigorously if necessary. For when the inquisitors badgered him for not rejecting Anne and clinging to the Boston church, he stood up and roared like a lion: "I know my wife better than I know any church and better than any church knows her, and I say she is one of God's saints!" With that he tucked her arm into his, glared fiercely at the astonished Bostonians, and stalked out. Shortly afterward, these officious busybodies skulked out of town, thoroughly cowed by our vigorous and unrepentant support of "an arch heretic." Aye, 'twill be a sad day for me when we leave; but where men lead, women must follow.

Will and the judge have gone prospecting in the shallop. I fear they will not be able to bear one another's company long enough to find a suitable location, for when they pushed off the judge had already taken charge and was ordering Will to do now this, now that. Will is long-suffering, but he will not turn the other cheek forever; and though he may not have quite so much money as the judge, he is by birth quite his equal and is likely to dump our friend into the bay—for a moment—if his patiencc wcars thin.

[*Third month*]

'Tis the end of the month and finally we are settled, temporarily, that is. All are housed in crude huts along the southwestern shore of Aquidneck, on the edge of a lovely but useless, mosquito-ridden swamp. I asked Will why he ever consented to this location, and he replied, as I expected, that he had finally agreed only because he was sick of the judge's carping. However, there is a clear, sweet spring above the swamp.

We have held our first town meeting, retaining our judge and elders as in Pocasset, and named our settlement "Newport" after the chief town on Isle of Wight. Both this island and the English one have great cliffs 'gainst which the waves thunder and crash (although our little village is on the bay side, protected by William Brenton's point of land), and are similar in shape.

Now that the highways, house lots, and farmlands have been laid out, we are all gradually becoming settled. The new sawmill turns out planks at a great rate, keeping our men busy raising walls and laying on rafters. Of course Mr. Easton built the first house—it's his mill!—and then the judge had to be housed in even more elaborate quarters than his Boston home. Many of us are using shingles instead of thatch for the roof and making our chimneys of brick rather than mud and logs, which caught fire so easily and caused such destruction that we were forced to find other materials. Our windows will be leaded glass, Will says, and we are going to have a really big house this time.

Will's grist mill will be ready when harvest comes; in the meantime he is buying numbers of horses, cows, sheep, and pigs. He also has an interest in the ship-building works and spends much time superintending the young apprentices there. Jane's boys would have enjoyed this work, but she finally made up her mind to stay behind in Pocasset with Anne. I did not urge her to come, for although she is just a poor, silly, ignorant woman, it still grieves me to remember the malicious gossip she started.

Word comes from Boston that a publishing firm has been established there. It is called the "Cambridge Press," and its assets consist of one small printing machine in a hut in Harvard Yard and a printer named Stephen Daye. Its books will of course be strictly censored.

The messenger also reported that one of the Boston inns has been designated as the official place to leave or pick up letters. Travelers will still carry the letters from town to town but are relieved of their responsibility when they reach the inn. This place is called a "post house."

The General Court, still meddling in every aspect of Bay life, has now forbidden the wearing of great (full) pants, broad shoulder bands, double ruffles on capes, and silk roses on shoes. The laws are meant, no doubt, not only for the spiritual benefit of the colony but also for its economic welfare—money not spent on frivolous luxuries can be used to support and expand the colony's own industries: food production, ship-building, fur-trading, and fishing, always fishing. Whatever should we all have done without the ubiquitous, prolific, cold-eyed cod—our mainstay in times of famine, our money-maker in times of plenty.

However, not all initiative has been stifled in Boston. One enterprising man has begun ferry service from Charlestown to Boston, and about time, too. The charge is four pennies per passenger, with horses either swimming or being ferried across in two canoes. Carriages must either be towed across or taken apart. 'Tis an imperfect system but better than nothing.

[*Ninth month*]

Will came home elated today from quarterly court, their deliberations and actions having been in accord with his own wishes, for a change. They have completely rejected theocratic government, embraced democracy, and pledged allegiance to King Charles. Furthermore, Pocasset, now called Portsmouth, and Newport have combined their separate governments for greater efficiency and protection. Coddington was elected governor and Will secretary.

All of us look forward with great joy to increased civic and religious harmony and financial advancement. Our trials have been many, but surely at last our prospects are brightening again. As for me, my greatest joy is the discovery that Will and I are to have another child.

[*First month, 1640*]

Our general court, in its first meeting of the new year, has issued a declaration stating formally that our government is to be a democracy with a majority of the freemen making the laws, and that no one "be accounted a delinquent for doctrine"—this latter assuring us religious liberty and freedom of conscience.

How wonderful it is to be alive in this glorious land! The past year has been marvellously good to us in many ways. Our settlement has prospered and grown strong, our people are well fed and clothed, we worship as we please and govern ourselves peacefully—what more could one ask?

[*Fourth month*]

Will and I have just returned from a visit to Portsmouth. I stayed a week with Anne, while Will and Sam went on to our island in the bay where we keep the sheep and pigs. Jane's boys went along to "beat the island," driving the foxes and wolves into pens and traps. Fortunately there were only a few and they seem not to have caused much damage. Here it is another story; they prowl the underbrush constantly and in great numbers, and our little shepherds and swineherds must ever be alert. The men will have a full-scale hunt as soon as the planting is done.

Will was very pleased with the increase in our flocks. "'Tis the mild, healthful climate, my dear," he declared. "The animals not only survived the winter in good condition, but the ewes are dropping twins and even triplets as our cows did on the farm, and the sows have large, healthy litters too. Why, even the number of deaths among our people has declined. Mayhap," he went on with a twinkle in his eye, "this prevalence of multiple births will extend to us as well."

"Oh, hush, Will, do stop teasing," I said, blushing. Of course the climate can't really have anything to do with such things.

Anne was full of talk and news, chattering constantly as she bustled about the house. "The Cambridge Press," she said, "that great enterprise in the cow pasture, has labored mightily and brought forth its first work, a volume called *The Whole Book of Psalms Faithfully Translated into English Metre*. Our old friends, John Eliot, Richard Mather, and Thomas Welde—remember his brother, dear Warden Welde?—are the editors. There is a copy on the shelf behind thee. Look at it and tell me thy opinion."

I glanced with interest through the volume and at last replied, "'Twill do very well, I think, for singing, though for reading 'tis rather stilted. Listen to the twenty-third psalm:

> The Lord to mee a shepheard is,
> want therefore shall not I.
> Hee in the folds of tender-grasse,

doth cause mee downe to lie:
To waters calme me gently leads
Restore my soule doth hee:

and so on."

Anne agreed. "I daresay it will be a great help to us all in meeting, although the old folks will still sing off tune. But at least we can all sing together now instead of the deacons singing out one line at a time and waiting for us to respond."

" 'Twill cut down on the length of service, too," I said unthinkingly.

"Mary, Mary," reproved Anne gently. "I fear thou art not yet as spiritually mature as thou might be."

I hurried to change the subject. "What other news is there?"

Anne smiled broadly at my embarrassment. "Well," she said, stirring the ragout carefully, "the population has reached twelve hundred—think of that! Ship-building goes on at a great pace, and our ships sail to Barbados, West Indies, Spain, and Madeira, carrying horses to those places and returning with wine and sugar; others carry tobacco from Virginia to Ireland and England and return with cargoes of textiles, clothes, and furniture. Ale is a penny a quart as is milk right from the cow, and Boston is building a new meetinghouse, with a steeple, more in keeping with its position as leader of the colonies. Remember how cold that dirt floor was in winter?"

"Aye, they can certainly use a new one," I declared. "Captain John Underhill, one of Boston's so-called heroes during the Pequod War, has outlived his usefulness to the colony in these days of peace, got into mischief, and been excommunicated for his sins, one of which was reputed to be adultery. I remember that he always did have a roving eye."

"I can speak to that," I said, blushing. "He often ogled me in meeting 'til the tipster poked him sharply, and was somewhat too courteous at our chance encounters in the streets. Indeed, we met so often I began to wonder if it really was by chance, and mentioned it to Will. After that we seldom met, and when we did he only muttered a greeting and hurried on."

Anne smiled. Picking up a skein of wool, she hooked it over my hands and began to wind it into a ball for knitting. "Harry Vane," she remarked after a few moments, "has written us a long letter relating all the most recent news from England."

"Dear Harry!" I exclaimed. "He was such a fine young man and had such a promising future here until he was called home. What has he been doing since then?"

"Well," said Anne, "after helping his father with his financial and political affairs for a bit—the elder Vane is active in Parliament, you know—he met and married a lovely girl from the North—high time for a bachelor of his years—and settled down to his philosophical and religious studies on the family estate. This spring he stood for Parliament, was elected, chosen joint treasurer of the navy, and in Fourth month was knighted. Isn't that fine?"

I agreed wholeheartedly, for both Will and I had been fond of Harry. "And what," I asked, "has become of Mr. Gorton?"

"Oh, dear," she laughed. "That man is a born troublemaker. I'll wager he has been arguing with someone about something ever since the day he lisped his first sentence. Not a Lecture day passes that he does not rise with great solemnity and dignity and put to our lay ministers some very disturbing question concerning theology: 'Is not the death of Christ merely symbolical? Is it not intended for man to communicate directly with Christ, not through church forms and observances? Is not the Godhead in reality one person instead of three? Is not immortality figurative, and heaven a condition of the soul?' Then when someone begins to reply, he interrupts repeatedly, and if the answer differs from his own views, he becomes abusive. Outside meeting he is just as opinionated about secular matters, still harping on the illegality of our government since we do not hold authorization from the king. He thinks he has a monopoly on truth and that the rest of us are ignoramuses and idiots. To put it mildly, he is a thoroughly unpleasant man."

"But can't you people do anything about him?"

"Not much, my dear," she replied. "Oh, the court might sentence him to the stocks as a public nuisance, for indeed he stops people on the street to argue and blocks the shop doors with his hangers-on. As for his strange beliefs, we must allow him the same freedom of conscience and expression that we wish for ourselves.

"By the way," she continued, "tell Will that Providence has finally succumbed to general custom and set up an organized government. They have selected a committee of five men to arbitrate all disputes for the community. 'Twill be a start anyway and end some of the wrangling there. And now," she said as several of the younger children skipped into the room, "we'd best leave off gossiping and feed these ravenous young ones. Didst finish thy sampler, little one?"

Susannah and Zuryell ran to her shrieking with joy, the girl proudly showing her completed handiwork, the younger boy clinging to her skirts. They each received a great hug and resounding kiss from their mother. Young William did not hang back either but clamored for recognition of his help in fetching and carrying for the carpenters. Mary and Anne left off scrubbing floors in the other rooms and helped to prepare the board. Their father appeared presently, in a somewhat more sedate manner, and was likewise greeted affectionately by Anne.

"Am I not a lucky man, Mary, with a wonderful wife and a houseful of fine children?" he asked happily.

"Oh, pshaw, Will," Anne laughed. " 'Tis I who am lucky. Who else would put up with my notions, my too-ready tongue, and my argumentative nature? No," she repeated seriously, "I am the lucky one, and what we should all do without our dear father and husband is more than I can imagine."

And so we talked and busied ourselves about the house; on Lecture day and First day Will and the boys worshiped with us; and whenever we had some free time we called on the sick with pitchers of broth or poultices of herbs, and varied our conversation to suit the patient's need, comforting this one with Scripture, regaling that one with the latest news, advising another from Anne's vast store of common sense and experience, and everywhere we were warmly received. Controversial though she be, Anne is yet a true saint and not without honor in her own land.

[*Seventh month*]

Oh bright, bright days! Next to the blue of Eighth month this is the most beautiful season of all, not even spring can surpass it. Now truly one can say with the psalmist: "The heavens declare the glory of God and the firmament sheweth his handiwork." Vivid asters and goldenrod gleam in lush emerald meadows, snow-white clouds drift through azure skies, salty breezes riffle the sparkling, white-capped waters of the bay, and the scent of new-mown hay is wafted on the inland airs. An orange moon climbs slowly through the black and velvet night, and all is quiet save for the yowling of a cat or the calling of the watchman as he cries the time and weather on his rounds. Then I snuggle closer to Will and offer up a little prayer of thanks for all that God has given us—our fine house, our sweet son in his trundle bed, and our lovely little daughter beside us in the cradle.

Mary, as Will insisted she be named, was born last month just as we moved into this house. Indeed, the little mite was more fortunate than we grown-ups, her cradle being in good condition; for we were forced to discard most of our other furniture as it had been ruined by the cave dampness of our early months on the island. I had ordered more pieces from England, but since the ship was delayed several weeks because of bad weather, Sam and I were forced to sit about the board in the kitchen, or on the scattered rugs which Mother had sent over earlier. There was always a good-natured race between Will and me to see which of us would sit in my great oak chair, still sturdy in spite of its many moves, but he usually won; for even if I got there first, no sooner had I ensconced myself comfortably when he recalled some added chore for me and I must reluctantly vacate the treasured seat.

The house is truly fine, with a spacious hall for entertaining at dinner or quilting bees, a large bedroom for our family, a commodious kitchen for cooking, spinning, weaving, whittling, candle-making, etc., and three small bedrooms upstairs, one of which Hope, our young serving girl, occupies. The floors are all sanded, and the windows are of glass. We have three chimneys, all of brick; 'tis a great extravagance, I chided Will, but he replied that brick was the safest, least combustible material, and as for the number, he was bound he'd be comfortable for once in the winter instead of shivering if he doffed his jacket and cloak.

Dear little Mary with her brown hair and eyes looks as much like me as Sam looks like his father. And she is such a good baby, sleeping soundly for hours and gazing about quietly for a time when she wakens. Sam loves to hold and rock her, for she smiles often at him and clutches his finger. Will thinks the world of her, too, and is always cuddling and kissing her when at home; and when he and Sam aren't crooning to her, I am. 'Tis a lucky thing Hope is here to see to the work!

Hope is a good, willing girl of thirteen whose parents perished during the great storm of '38, and who had been shunted from house to house and starved until she simply could not stand it a moment longer and tried to stow away on board a ship returning to England. Heaven knows what she intended to do there, as she has no living relations. Luckily Sam found her as he was exploring an empty hold one day while Will conducted some business with the captain. And Will, bless his dear, soft heart, took pity on her and pledged to the court to be responsible for her. He said it was to have someone to help me here, but I know 'twas also because he cannot bear to see a child suffer.

There was much excitement last month during quarterly court. After the usual financial reports and proposals, the court voted to set aside some land here in Newport for the establishment of a public school, the first of its kind in the area, although of course we have several private schools. This will be to teach the poorer children reading, writing, and some trade. Robert Lenthall, a clergyman, was admitted as a freeman and appointed master of the school at a mere pittance.

That disposed of, the trial of Sam Gorton's maid began. It seems that Goodwife Sherman, accustomed to pasturing her cow in Mr. G.'s field, was set upon one day by his maid, a sturdy, young girl, the same one caught smiling in Plymouth church. This maid beat the poor old soul vigorously with her cow stick, calling her names and warning her to graze her cow elsewhere. Goody Sherman of course complained bitterly to Deputy Governor Brenton. Having heard her story and examined her bruises, the Deputy then questioned the maid and, dissatisfied with her replies, bound her over to the court. At quarterly meeting she appeared for a hearing with Mr. G. as her advocate, a rare enough circumstance, since few accused have any kind of representation in these days and times, either here or at home.

Each witness testified in favor of the plaintiff concerning her poverty, advanced age, good character, and the severe aches and bruises she had sustained. But for the maid's character they had nothing good to say. Furthermore, it was brought out that the field in question was actually a part of the public domain.

Upon hearing this, Mr. G. lost all self-restraint. He leaped to his feet and lectured the court roundly. "This entire island is public domain," he thundered. "No royal patent has ever been issued for this colony, no trading company has ever been set up in England to exploit and explore this territory. This ridiculous court with its puling plaintiffs and ignorant officers prating of justice exists only in your own minds. To it no power has ever been delegated by the king to deed lands, to tax, to govern, to chastise. Therefore all this land is public, available freely to any who wish to settle on it. And this court," he sneered, "is not a real court—'tis a play court, and you are children playing at being men. Your witnesses are liars and ignoramuses, and your officers are wicked perverters of justice!"

At this point, cries of "Hear! Hear!" and "Give it to 'em, Sam!" were heard from Wickes and Holden.

Before he could take breath and continue his tirade, Governor Coddington exclaimed indignantly, "That will do, Sir! Any further hindrance of these proceedings, or derogatory remarks concerning the court's intelligence and integrity, will be severely dealt with. You will confine yourself to proper questioning or be removed. Next witness, please."

As the next witness placed his hand on the Book for the oath, Mr. G. again bounded from his seat. Smarting from the governor's rebuke and too obstinate to curb his tongue and temper, he blazed forth anew. "An oath is an idol to you," he jeered. "You worship and bow down before it as the Israelites worshiped the golden calf, and as the Babylonians bowed to Nebuchadnezzar's image of gold. Do you honestly believe that the blackest knave in Christendom will speak the truth merely because he takes an oath and kisses the Book? Yea, if he kiss fifty Books? Indeed," he railed, "we all know there are false swearers, and who is to say, 'This one sweareth truly,' or 'That one sweareth falsely'? But what can one expect"—he glared at Brenton, the man who had defeated him for deputy—"when the blind lead the blind, when incompetents and misfits insinuate their way into positions of power through chicanery and bribes, and when"—but here he was brought up short. Livid with rage, Deputy Brenton sprang at him, fists clenched.

"Order!" cried Coddington, "Constable, seize Mr. Gorton and commit him to the gaol!"

Both Clarke and Sanford rushed forward, along with Sergeant Bull. At the same time Wickes, Holden, and several other Gortonists rushed to protect their leader. Belligerently they massed about him. The peace officers paused as Gorton raised his hand in a warning gesture.

"Wait!" he commanded. "What is the charge?"

"Mutinous and seditious speeches!" roared Coddington, who had little enough patience at ordinary times and none at all when crossed.

Sam raised his eyebrows, lowered his voice, and pretended incredulity. "*You* indict *me* for these crimes? These are crimes against a government, an established, recognized government. But you poor, sniveling,"—now he increased both tempo and volume of his voice—"whimpering caricatures of men, you are naught but traitors to the king!"

At this inflammatory charge the entire company sprang up. Shaking with anger, Coddington plunged forward. "You that are for the king, lay hold on Gorton!" he thundered.

"You that are for the king, lay hold on Coddington!" retorted Gorton boldly.

As the governor made to seize Mr. G. about the neck, Wickes shoved him violently and sent him crashing to the floor. Instantly the governor's partisans pressed forward upon the Gortonists. Will leaped from his desk where he had been taking notes and joined heartily in the affray. In a few moments, however, it was all over, with the Gortonists sprawled on the floor, securely pinioned by the assistants and officers of the court.

Someone fetched a bucket of water to douse the governor. Spluttering weakly, he sat up and, seeing the situation well in hand, mustered the remnants of his dignity. "Mr. Wickes is sentenced to the stocks for twenty-four hours," he groaned, massaging his skull tenderly, "and Mr. Gorton to the whipping post for twenty lashes, then to be banished from our colony within six weeks. If there is no disagreement or further business, this court stands adjourned."

Not a voice was raised in protest and the meeting broke up, the men murmuring dazedly together at these shocking events, or grinning sheepishly over their bumps and bruises. Will, although not fond of the governor, nevertheless offered him his arm, and Mr. C. limped painfully up Thames Street to the soothing ministrations of his wife. Will also required a small poultice of herbs, as there was a large purple and yellow discoloration rapidly appearing about one eye.

He told his story with relish, and when I chided him on his enthusiastic account of the melee, he indignantly declared that there was nothing to be ashamed of in fighting for the preservation of law and order, and that it was one of the basic duties of each citizen to defend his duly constituted government. Dear Will, middle-aged, respectable, devout though he is, it is plain that he thoroughly enjoyed this brawling and still has that adventurous spirit which brought us from England to Boston and from there to Aquiday. "The Isle of Peace"—how fitting a name it was when only the Narragansetts dwelt here and how incongruous since the arrival of Christian settlers!

1641-1643

[*First month, 1641*]

Our Boston friends write that the Harvard Press, encouraged by the success of its psalm book, recently issued another work, a small pamphlet entitled *The New England Almanack.* It contains a calendar, predictions of the weather, remedies for sick cattle, instructions for growing crops, and the signs of the zodiac by which one may conduct one's personal and business affairs.

The same friends also report that Nathaniel Eaton, the Harvard master, and his wife have finally been discharged for beating the students and feeding them wormy and poorly cooked victuals. These misdeeds also brought him excommunication from Mr. Shepard's church. Really, they are excommunicating for just anything these days!

News from England is most disturbing. Last year the king, himself a Scotsman, had ordered all Scots to forsake their Presbyterianism for the Anglican Church. Naturally they rebelled. Being short of money to fight these recalcitrants, Charles was forced to call his first parliament since 1629. Under Harry Vane's leadership, the Puritan and merchant M.P.'s vigorously opposed his demands for tax legislation, and the entire body was summarily dissolved after sitting only three weeks. Charles then resumed his old practice of levying taxes, billeting soldiers in private homes, and imprisoning citizens illegally, all in direct contravention of the Petition of Right of 1628 which specifically denied him the "divine" rights he claimed and required him to act only with parliament's approval. The revolt has spread now until all England is split with bitter dissension. Puritans and other independents refuse flatly to empty their purses, feed the king's men, or accept a state religion. Archbishop Laud has doubled his spies and heretic-hunters, and the prisons are overflowing. Nevertheless, the rebels stand fast. Indeed, their firm opposition has forced Charles to call another parliament. Since independent M.P.'s outnumber the royalists, they appear likely to sit for some time, and Harry Vane is with them. Oddly enough it is reported that he is a follower of the "Seekers," that strange religious sect Roger Williams now embraces. But then Harry always was an eager student of philosophy and religion.

Here at home also religion continues to be a cause of controversy. Nicholas Easton, our prosperous tanner and sawmill owner, asserted recently that all things being made and formed by God, God is therefore the author of sin also. In this opinion he was joined by John Coggeshall and Mr. Coddington. John Clarke, schoolmaster Lenthall, and Will argued against this, saying that since God is perfect and without evil he could not create evil. Mr. Easton retorted that an omnipotent God can do anything and that evil was created to test us. Mr. Lenthall then insisted that, since God created us in his own image, he desires only good for us; furthermore, that the Perfect Being has no prior knowledge of evil, and that it was Satan, fallen from grace, who brought sin into the world. These "fallacies" were quickly pounced on and worried by our elderly but alert tanner.

"Of course God knew about evil," he declared. "We have his own words to Adam, 'Of every tree of the garden thou mayest freely eat: but of the tree of the knowledge of good and evil, thou shalt not eat of it. . . .' Since God made every beast, fowl, and tree, it is obvious he also made this particular tree and thus created evil. As for Satan," he scoffed, "how could a former angel know anything about sin, or know enough *to* sin, unless he learned it from the Creator?"

And there the matter rested. Mr. Lenthall took himself off for England shortly afterwards, plaintively remarking that he preferred the more conventional practice of religion —meaning that at home no one would dare raise such questions with the clergy. However, his quite inadequate salary as schoolmaster undoubtedly also had much to do with his departure.

Will still argues the point privately at times and even concedes there might be some merit for the other view, but his antipathy to Mr. Coddington prevents his agreeing with him on anything. I do wish they could be friends, but it seems that Mr. C. grows more arrogant and irascible as time goes on. How does his wife get along with him? She herself is a pleasant, mild-mannered woman.

Our friends in Providence also continue to experience growing pains. They have felt compelled to deny admission to Sam Gorton and his followers for being public nuisances. The group has moved on to the Pawtucket River area, said to be common land belonging to the Bay colony.

[*Fifth month*]

The political situation in England continues to deteriorate. Charles is faced on the one hand with an obstinate, unfriendly parliament, and on the other with an increasingly unruly and rebellious multitude of Puritans. His demands, his edicts, his proclamations go unheeded. When one recalcitrant is jailed, two step forward to carry on; Laud is imprisoned in the Tower and charged by parliament with treason; London has become a seething cauldron of venom and intrigue, and sturdy Scotland openly arms her stolid sons for freedom's fight.

Our own fortunes prosper—fine flocks and herds, a busy mill, good health, loving friends. But Mr. C. remains a large, sharp thorn in our flesh. His cattle continually wander into our pastures or into the swamp whence Will must rescue them on his daily ride about the farm. 'Tis all very exciting to Sam, who canters along on his pony, but a great nuisance to Will. "Why can't the man keep his fences in repair?" he grumbles; and answers himself, "Because he's too busy dabbling in politics, that's why."

[*Eighth month*]

Well, the Hutchinsons are still carrying on their feud with Boston. It seems that William Collins, the youthful minister who married young Anne, was so distraught over the continuing persecution of his mother-in-law that he let loose a furious fusillade of criticism at the Boston clergy, denouncing them in a letter as anti-Christian and deriding the king as "King of Babylon." Having received a typically condescending and irritating reply, he recklessly set out to grapple with the dragons at their lair. With him went Francis Hutchinson, a hotheaded stripling of twenty-one.

Charging manfully into Boston, they were quickly unhorsed by the local constables and haled before the governor and elders. They might yet have escaped with only a verbal reprimand; but young Francis, burning with righteous indignation and fierce loyalty, threw off the shackles of self-control and reviled the assembly with, alas, some rather strong language. Fired by his example, William repeated his criticisms, embellishing his tirade with one or two more uncomplimentary remarks.

Such audacity was too much for the proud authoritarians. The brave knights were hustled off to a vile dungeon for several months' repentance and fined twenty shillings each. However, Anne's friends in Boston, by maneuvering tactfully and emphasizing the youth of the prisoners, were able to secure their release after three weeks. A reduced fine was quickly paid, the subdued knights were rushed to the colony's borders, and everyone—parents, friends, and ministers alike—sighed with relief.

I have treated the episode lightly, but they were indeed brave boys and I sincerely applaud their spirit, if not their method.

[*Ninth month*]

Sam Gorton is again—or, more accurately, still—embroiled in controversy with the authorities. Denied admittance to Providence, he and his followers settled on the Pawtucket River lands, which they understood were in the public domain. What was their astonishment recently when the William Harris group from Providence moved in and curtly ordered them off the land! Francis Weston, whose property was most directly concerned, indignantly appealed to Roger Williams for justice. Looking up the deed, the board of arbitrators found that the land had indeed been assigned to Harris and his friends for grazing land, and that an additional clause confirming this had been dated 1639 and signed by Miantonomo. There was much discussion about this clause as no one but Harris remembered anything about it. However, the board eventually agreed that the title was clear and ordered Mr. Weston to pay Harris £15 in cash, cattle, or commodities. Suspecting trickery of some kind, Sam Gorton advised him not to pay. The board then attempted to attach Weston's cattle. At once the Gortonists raised a tremendous outcry and did not fail to include those so foolhardy as to accompany the constables.

Sam declared that it was a struggle for liberty: of the poor, landless, nonvoting freemen versus the rich, voting landholders. Furthermore, he asserted, the deed and its codicil were obvious forgeries and therefore the disputed land was actually public land. Thus none of its occupants had any legal recourse against another group.

At the mention of forgery the Harrisites quickly abandoned their appeals to Providence and turned instead to Massachusetts for help. Boston replied in a terse letter that she would assist only if they made themselves subject either to her own jurisdiction or that of Plymouth—she could not spare the time, effort, expense, or men to protect settlers who contributed nothing to her coffers.

The matter is as yet unsettled, with an uneasy truce prevailing between the two factions.

[*First month, 1642*]

Will had his hair trimmed today and Sam his. I nearly wept to have those lovely blond curls cut off. They went to Mr. Jeffries' shop, as he is licensed now to practice chirurgy. His red and white striped pole, denoting blood and bandages, informs even the uneducated and illiterate that he may let blood, treat minor ills, clip beards, and trim hair. He talked incessantly, Will said, about politics, industry, crops, and the weather. The only interesting bit of news he related was about Plymouth, Will reported. They are having a widespread outbreak of crime—swearing, smoking, robbery, pilfering, drunkenness, assault, and adultery. The last-named crime occurs quite frequently in spite of all the religious fervor supposedly extant.

[*Third month*]

News comes from Portsmouth that Will Hutchinson has died, and that Anne wishes me to visit her. I shall go tomorrow. Hope can look after the older children well enough and let some of the other work go.

It is good to be home again—to hug my babies and to feel Will's strong arm about my shoulders once more.

Anne was outwardly calm and contained for the most part, but at times she seemed dazed and unsure of herself. More than once she stopped in the middle of a sentence to gaze unseeing into space, or picked up some object only to replace it unused. She talked eagerly to me of Will, how kind and quiet and long-suffering he had been, always encouraging her, never criticizing or hindering, though her wishes and "calls" had meant leaving his prosperous business and congenial friends. She described his illness—a severe cold caught while out in a storm—and how she nursed him constantly; but for all her skill and love, she who had saved so many others could not save him.

"And so he is gone," she sighed, "my comfort and my mainstay. Whatever shall we do without him?"

But I could only repeat to her what she had said to

others: "Trust in the Lord. He will sustain thee and lead thee into new paths of service." Her brave, unconquerable spirit will carry her on, I am sure, but into which paths we cannot know; mayhap toward more trials and tribulations; or toward peaceful declining years in the midst of a loving family. It is not given to us to perceive the future. We can only trust in God and follow his leadings.

[*Fourth month*]

Roger Williams spent the night with us recently on his way to Manhattan Island. The Dutch there, too greedy to be satisfied with buying land cheaply from the Indians, have attacked several friendly tribes and demanded tribute from them. When the Indians not only refused to pay but retaliated with raids on white settlements, the Dutch belatedly realized their tragic mistake and besought Mr. Williams to act as intermediary. From there he will take ship for England in an effort to obtain a royal charter for the Providence lands. Evidently some of Sam Gorton's words made a favorable impression on the townfolk.

[*Sixth month*]

My heart is heavy with sadness and foreboding. Anne has moved her family to Long Island. They arrived one morning along with the Collinses and several other Portsmouth families, purchased supplies, hired a boat, spent the night with us, and departed next day. Anne was in good spirits, restraining her enthusiasm with difficulty. Portsmouth was unbearable without Will, she confided, and she hoped that a new location, new friends, and new opportunities would restore her to her former useful and efficient way of life.

I was aghast that they should venture into such hostile

territory, for the Indians there are fierce indeed, and Mr. Williams was not entirely successful in his mission to them. But Anne laughed and said, "Don't worry. We shall win them over soon; and after they become friends, we shall convert them. There is work to be done, and I have always been a worker!"

Will lectured her severely about forsaking English rule for the Dutch. She heard him out, then asked quietly, "Could the Dutch really be any more cruel to me than my own countrymen have been? Could their slanders and jeers, their excommunication hurt me any worse than did the Boston church? Nay, friend," she said, a smile of incomparable sweetness lighting her countenance, "my allegiance is to God, and to him only do I look for protection."

So we let the matter rest. Anne requires a great purpose to occupy her hands and heart; and the savages need a minister of outstanding ability and courage. It was a clear call in the name of Christ.

And yet I cannot rid my mind of all its vague fears and apprehensions. Will tries to cheer me by saying they are due to my condition (for I am with child again); but I cannot help feeling that Anne's choice of the path to hardship and danger, rather than to safety and comfort, portends only an ominous future. God be with her and with those other brave souls. I shall miss her sorely.

[*Eighth month*]

Alas, the Bay colony has its own troubles with Indians, and there is no telling what horrors they may stir up for the rest of us. Our good friend, and theirs too, Miantonomo, chief of the Narragansetts, was accused recently of conspiring to destroy all the New England and Dutch settlements. Although this good man was largely responsible for the defeat of the Pequods and has always been on excellent terms with all the English authorities, the Bay rulers believed these vicious rumors and ordered him to Boston. Somewhat bewildered by the white man's ingratitude and lack of trust, Miantonomo nevertheless appeared and produced witnesses who vouched for his good character and peaceful intentions. He then demanded to meet his accusers, declaring that either he or they should be put to death. Of course, governor Winthrop could not point to any particular man with certainty, although like us he may well have suspected the chief's long-time enemy, Uncas, chief of the Mohicans. Further impressed by the Indian's understanding of justice and integrity and his forthright, unequivocal protestations of innocence, the governor released him without further ado. However, I fear this is the beginning of more trouble between the two races.

In Massachusetts a new law makes parents responsible for their children's learning to read and write; and Harvard College has conferred its first degree. New Haven has employed Ezekiel Cheever as its first schoolmaster. Most of the schools charge a small fee for firewood and supplies, but as this is not required of the poorer students, the schools are essentially free. Their number is growing, but Will still maintains they are a mistake. "Having all levels of income and intelligence together may be considered democratic by some," he growls, "but I say the stupid pupils will only slow down the bright ones. Is that democratic? And furthermore . . ."

"Is it fair for poor, bright boys to have no chance for an education?" I interrupted.

"Of course not," he retorted testily, "but we can set up a fund for them in the private schools. What I wanted to add when I was interrupted is that we are setting a dangerous precedent in expecting the government to pay for our schools and educate our indigent people. Soon we shall expect the government to help us when we are old, or sick, or lose our crops. All this so-called aid will only lead to higher taxes and less freedom!" So he stalked off angrily, to harangue his customers at the mill, no doubt.

The Harrisites—or "parasites," as Sam Gorton refers to them—have finally cast their lot with Massachusetts. Sam was furious at what he considered Boston's treachery and disregard of common law. Never at a loss for words, he scribbled off a twenty-five-page letter of scathing vituperation and sent it by special messenger to the governor.

Having thus thoroughly vented his spleen, he sought out Miantonomo, purchased extensive lands, packed up his family, and moved to Shawomet, twelve miles away across the river and quite beyond the Massachusetts borders.

From England the news is dreadful indeed: Civil war has broken out. Rebuffed by an obstinate and parsimonious parliament, and beset by Protestant leaders demanding toleration and a Presbyterian national church, the king one day attempted to seize five of his most vociferous opponents in Parliament. They stoutly resisted this shocking outrage, and under the leadership of Oliver Cromwell quickly formed their own army. Supported by vast numbers of Puritans, Independents, and merchants (who naturally stand to lose great sums if Charles is permitted to tax and seize at will), Cromwell was not content merely to protect his fellow members, but pressed forward with an attack on the king's own forces. Although Charles is supported by the nobility, gentry, and clergy (as might be expected), he has not yet been able to pry them loose from their fat purses.

The rebels have shorn their long locks, they have hurled from them the curly wigs of aristocracy and privilege, they have put on the helmet and breastplate of righteousness; and it may well be that the religious fervor and determination of these Roundheads will result in victory for all freedom-loving Englishmen.

[*Twelfth month*]

The court at Boston, incensed that anyone should give asylum to the heretical Gortonists, last month summoned Miantonomo to appear before it and explain his willful disregard of the court's wishes! In his absence the wily Uncas attacked and slew a number of the Narragansetts in Connecticut.

Appealing to the authorities there, the chief was rebuffed. He turned then to Boston, where his pleas for aid and advice were received even more coldly by those very men who had benefited so greatly and for so long by his own cooperation. Sick at heart, he returned home to ponder his choices: to leave his people unavenged, or to break his treaty with the English and make war on Uncas. Whatever decision he makes, there can be only suffering and death ahead for his people. For if they ignore the Mohicans, Uncas will attack again and again; and if they seek revenge, the English will declare war and drive them from their homeland. His decision is a hard one indeed, rendered doubly so by the absence of Roger Williams, his closest friend. There are troubled times ahead.

[*Third month, 1643*]

This month, at the instigation of Thomas Hooker, has been formed the United Colonies of New England (consisting of the Massachusetts, Plymouth, Connecticut, and

New Haven colonies), for mutual security against the Indians and for "preserving and propagating the truth and liberties of the gospel," the first such union in our new land. What it amounts to, Will says, is further control of religion, and in a dastardly way, too; for if a community besieged by savages is deemed to have strayed from the truth as propounded by the leaders of the United Colonies, not a hand will be lifted to save them. The participating colonies have also agreed to return one another's runaway servants and escaped prisoners, and to make treaties with the Dutch and French. I doubt England will permit *that* for very long!

[*Fifth month*]

Relations with the Indians are deteriorating rapidly, thanks to the stupidity of Boston and the greed of the Pawtucket settlers. It seems that William and Benjamin Arnold had been secretly buying Shawomet land from one of the local sachems. If they could have the Gorton deed nullified and the land placed under Massachusetts' jurisdiction, they would be sole owners of Shawomet and much of Pawtucket, and wealthy men indeed. They therefore craftily persuaded two other sachems, Pumham and Sacononoco, that they had been forced to sign the Gorton deed and been defrauded of property and wampum alike by Gorton and their own chief. With Benjamin's encouragement they took their grievances to Boston.

The authorities were elated: Here was an excellent way to get at that arch heretic, Sam Gorton, and teach him that he could not flout their divinely instituted power. They quickly ordered both Miantonomo and Gorton to appear in court. The chief, willing as always, made his appearance and asserted strongly that local sachems had always heretofore acknowledged the chief's authority to wage war, to sign treaties, to sell land. The court, knowing this to be so, never having deigned to deal with anyone less than a chief, itself, yet pretended it must question the sachems; and upon doing so, speedily accepted their barefaced lies as truth and signed the treaty encompassing their lands.

Mr. Gorton, wary and suspicious, had prudently remained at home. Upon hearing the outcome, however, he did write another lengthy missive denouncing elders and magistrates for what he felt was unwarranted and unchristian persecution, stating defiantly that he and his men were ready to fight if anyone attempted to remove them from their legally purchased property.

The wily elders took no overt notice of this but slyly inflamed the two sachems against the "heretics and squatters." Returning home full of indignation, Pumham and Sacononoco began to harass the settlers: shooting their cattle, stoning the beasts, and stealing them. The fiery Gortonists immediately retaliated so effectively that the Arnolds cried for help. Gorton dashed off another scathing letter. Massachusetts replied that an investigating committee would be sent to settle the matter. Gorton warned them not to set foot on his land, and so on.

Meanwhile, Miantonomo, having pondered his own problems long and hard, at last decided that the course of honor for him lay not with the treacherous English and their worthless treaties but with his own people and with vengeance for their slain brothers. He attacked the Mohicans savagely. Uncas, outnumbered two to one, requested private combat—a contest between himself and his rival—in order to prevent the slaughter of his men. Miantonomo refused. It was a tragic mistake.

Fighting desperately, Uncas routed his foes and captured his rival. Custom gave him the right to kill the chief, but Uncas led his captive instead to Hartford for sentencing. There the court found Miantonomo guilty of violating his treaty with the English—of course they did not condemn themselves for failing him when he sought their aid—and sentenced him to die. He was returned to Uncas and never seen thereafter.

Thus did this noble friend go to an untimely, ill-deserved death. Ever courteous, helpful, loyal to his true English friends, an inspiring example of Roger Williams' ideal in his selfless efforts among the Indians, a Christian gentleman—all these he was. May his name and memory live forever in our grateful hearts. And may the crafty heathen Uncas burn in Hell!

[*Sixth month*]

"My heart is sore pained within me: and the terrors of death are fallen upon me. Fearfulness and trembling are come upon me, and horror hath overwhelmed me." Affliction and anguish are mine, and I am swallowed up with sorrow. . . . How poignantly the words of the psalmist speak to my condition! They roar in my ears during the day and lie heavily on my heart in the night. For Anne Hutchinson is dead! Slain by the savages they only sought to aid, she and her family perished in the cause of love and brotherhood. Only ten-year-old Susannah survived, and she was carried off by the murderers.

So has passed to everlasting life my dearest friend and God's true saint. No pen can write, no tongue can tell how much her love has meant to me, how much her faith and courage have sustained me. Life's journey led her, unswerving, through the straits of calumny and slander, down the dark valleys of death, up the craggy paths of righteousness to the pinnacle of salvation. Though I stumble and falter, God grant I may never betray the faith she taught me.

And so, good-bye, dear Anne. Until we meet beyond, good-bye.

[*Ninth month*]

Life must go on, of course; and though I grieve constantly for Anne, I also rejoice that she is now spared further suffering and persecution. The hatred and malice of the Boston ministers have followed her even to the grave, for when Thomas Welde learned of her death, he only sneered callously: "I have never heard of any other such slaughter by those Indians. Therefore God's hand is apparent in this tragedy. He has picked this wretched woman and her followers to be examples of what befalls those who stray in thought and deed from his prescribed paths."

Not one word did he speak about her many good works, her sincerity, her unfaltering faith. My heart is bitter indeed toward him and his sanctimonious, canting brethren. God must forgive them, for I never shall.

Not only are charity and justice alien to their characters, but their greed and duplicity are boundless. Writing to Will Coddington, Roger Williams reveals that Thomas Welde and Hugh Peter had hurried to London as soon as they learned the purpose of his voyage. Through their influence they secured the signatures of nine parliamentary commissioners for a Narragansett patent which would have given all our lands to Boston! It was only through the intervention of Pym, Cromwell, and Harry Vane that this patent was overridden and our own application approved. This patent unites the Aquidneck towns with Providence, fixes our boundaries, and gives us full power to govern ourselves, provided our punishments, laws, and constitution conform to those of England.

Will snorted at the terms. "Much good this patent will be if we must look to the old country for everything we wish to do. We might as well have a royal governor here to order us about!"

But at least it is a start, and we shall be happier without any such overseers. Let us hope too that the leaders of the Bay colony will now abandon their designs on our lives and property, although if they do I suspect it will only be for another scheme to torment us.

Sam Gorton and his colony are still being plagued by Indian attacks, while Boston considers the best means of how to subdue this irrepressible gadfly.

1644-1648

[*First month, 1644*]

What fiends these preachers are! What gross evil they do perpetrate in the holy name of God! The poor Gortonists have now felt the furious sting of their lash.

Warned by old Canonicus' lookouts that armed forces were marching on them, Gorton prepared to defend his flock. Some of the women, heavy with child, fled toward Providence, only to perish in the snowy drifts. The rest of the tiny band crowded together in a rude house near the mill race, determined to resist. When they saw the force arrayed against them, however, they asked for a parley.

"Let us declare a truce while the matter is referred to England. Let the king's men decide," Sam proposed.

"What! so you can have time to prepare new evidence?" jeered William Harris. (Was that his own guilty conscience speaking?)

"Besides, you are all heretics," cried Mr. Wilson, who had come along as spiritual adviser. "You must be shut away from good, decent folk lest you contaminate and seduce them with your vile arguments. Recant, repent, or it shall go hard with you indeed!"

At these inflammatory and false accusations, Sam indignantly broke off the parley. "The Devil take you and your good, decent folk!" he stormed and stamped back to the house as if he were grinding the pastor and William Harris beneath his heel at each step.

Conferring with his men, Sam made a difficult decision. "Brothers and sisters," he said quietly, "we are in the right in this matter. We also know our theological beliefs are in accord with the Bible. If there be any here who wish to recant or otherwise yield themselves to the—ahem—*tender* mercies of our foe, let them be gone now." Since no one moved, he continued. "Some of our people have already died in this cause, for it is too much to hope that all our women reached safety. Therefore, I say, let there be no more lives lost by our actions. If the enemy wish to attack, they shall take the burden of our blood upon themselves. We shall not resist. How say you?"

Solemnly they agreed. They had not long to wait, for the enemy did choose to attack, with booming muskets and flaming arrows. The thatch roof blazed up at once and threatened to engulf the Gortonists, but a Providential wind blew out the fire. The damage made the house untenable, however, and the Gortonists reluctantly sought another truce.

Wilson demanded that they go in chains to Boston; but Captain Cook, knowing them to be honorable men, required only their word and gave them safe conduct as free men to that city. Harris remained behind to seize the cattle and divide them with Arnold.

Arriving in Boston the little band was closely watched, although no attempt was made to gaol them. All Boston buzzed over the "great victory" and "daring capture" of these "dangerous renegades and apostates," and large numbers of people crowded into the meetinghouse for the trial.

There was considerable disappointment, therefore, when the ministers could find no heresy, no apostasy in Sam's religious views. The death sentence obviously could not be imposed. Nevertheless, to assuage their own mortification, the clergy ordered these innocent people to wear leg irons, to settle far apart from one another, and not to preach or write on religious themes on pain of death! They were then banished not only from Boston, but also from Providence, the patent not having become official yet and Boston still claiming jurisdiction there.

But Sam, though bloody and battered, was not the type to slink off and lick his wounds at anyone's command. Instead he defiantly gathered his flock about him once more and journeyed to Portsmouth for a brief respite. This town, which had scoffed at his preaching a few years earlier, now welcomed him as a martyr and offered him sanctuary for as long as he cared to stay. Overwhelmed by this kindness after his many trials and weary of strife, he has not ridiculed their courts or government once nor pressed his views publicly on any unwilling ear. He is respected throughout the town, and he himself respects the rights of others. May he live comfortably and securely now among his neighbors, full of honor and blessed by divine Providence with prosperity and peace.

General Court this month did change the name of our island. Thinking perhaps that "Isle of Peace" was not quite the suitable name it had been, they decided on "Isle of Rhodes," after the one described in Hakluyt's Voyages as covered with roses. While we do have many such flowers, it is the scarlet pimpernel which blossoms in profusion here, and 'twas either the abundance of this flower or possibly the red-hued cliffs which led the Dutch some time ago to refer to the place as "Rhode (meaning red) Island." Most of us are using the Dutch form already, as 'tis somewhat shorter than the other.

Roger Williams writes that the Narragansett patent takes effect this month, and we are now quite safe from the rapacious tentacles of Massachusetts—unless by some unhappy chance King Charles should beat back Cromwell's forces. This is not likely however, for Charles's treasury is so low that the queen has had to sell her jewels in Holland in order to replenish the royal purse.

[*Tenth month*]

Mr. Williams returned from England several months ago, having accomplished his mission. Now that the Plantations are assured of democratic self-government, Mr. Williams has established a trading post for the mutual benefit of colonists and redmen. It will be a convenient base for his Indian language studies and his preaching to the Narragansetts. (How greatly missionaries are needed throughout the land! Ony a month or two ago brutal savages slaughtered three hundred of our countrymen in Jamestown Colony.) His townfolk will miss him sorely, but as he is a great letter-writer he will continue to maintain close ties with us all—that is, if they ever reimburse him for his great expenses overseas.

Mother writes that Sam Gorton spent several days with her recently on his way to London. Though now the most peaceable of men (and so honored by his fellowmen that they elected him magistrate), he still is persecuted. It seems that after the Boston-Gorton affair of last winter, Canonicus and his followers decided that Sam was stronger than the Puritans, and that they would therefore follow his example and submit to English rule rather than Bay government. Dismayed at this rebuff, Mr. Winthrop requested Will Coddington to send Sam back to Boston for heaven-knows-what punishment, although it was certainly not Sam's fault that the Indians could recognize a good man and a right cause when they saw them. However, although our autocratic leader might have wished to comply, he certainly did not have the power to do so, nor would he have dared. Sam is too popular now on the island to be so shamefully mistreated. Massachusetts then complained to the parliamentary commission, and so Sam must appear before them and plead for the right to live in a free colony and influence any who choose to listen. Admiral Penn will intercede for him wherever possible, Mother says.

Although it is wicked of me, I cannot help gloating over the latest gossip from Boston: Valentine Hill, a merchant, has foreclosed the mortgage on John Winthrop's house!

[*Seventh month, 1645*]

Journeying to Boston recently we found many changes. The population has grown so much that the inhabitants no longer are able to have orchard and garden on the house lot; all houses are pressed so closely together that there is scarcely room to pass between. Glass windows are common now, and the houses themselves are generally larger than when we were there.

There was much gossip in the city about the prevalence of witches both here and in Europe. While no one has yet been put to death in the Bay colony, there are several who are looked upon with suspicion. My heart trembles for them. Now that there are no longer any religious rebels there to hound and root out, someone else must be sacrificed to satisfy the malevolent and perverted lusts masquerading as morality.

Of course there are some elderly or eccentric people who are fascinated by the supposed powers of those who practice the occult arts, and who really come to believe that those people belong to Satan. Nothing can be done for these wretched victims. But for such educated and influential persons as Francis Bacon and Sir Thomas Browne to claim they have proved the existence of witches is more than the law should allow. However, the king's own father not only wrote a treatise "proving" demonology but he also devised various methods of testing for witches. One of these is to wrap the suspect in a sheet and toss her into a pond; water, being the element of baptism, would reject any "unsaved" body, so that anyone who floats must be guilty. The innocent, of course, would be accorded a proper and "Christian" burial.

Remembering the vicious gossip which Jane Hawkins had started after our own little baby was born dead, I confided my uneasiness to Will. As usual, his sensible attitude comforted me. "They may whisper about thee night and day, my dear, but they would never dare to act against the wife of a man who holds a responsible public office and a heavy purse!" And 'tis truly so; for although these things are not quite so important in Newport, they are indeed decisive in this Bay community where the social, economic, political, and religious structures remain as rigid as the day it was begun.

Further news is that Oliver Cromwell and his hymn-singing troops have routed the royalists again at Naseby, causing Charles to flee to Scotland. Why the king chose this region instead of one more sympathetic to the established church is difficult to understand. For the Scots, good Presbyterians that they are, seized him and returned him to Parliament. Hustled off to the Tower, he now awaits bravely whatever the future may hold.

There is plenty of room in the Tower for him, since a former resident, fervent heretic-hunter William Laud, was beheaded not long ago; and while I abhorred the man for his cruel persecutions, I must agree with Will that the charge against him of treason was never proved and that the sentence of death was harsh indeed.

These two events, the imprisonment of Charles and the death of Laud, have been hailed throughout England and the colonies as symbolic of new political and religious freedom. Thus many minds in Boston turned naturally to another figure symbolic of those same freedoms—Anne Hutchinson. Desiring to acknowledge her immeasurable contribution and our abiding love, we planned at first to honor her memory in one of the homes; but with so many friends gathering to participate, we proceeded instead to the Common. Here we stood in silent prayer, until first one, then another, was moved to speak the message of his heart.

I had never spoken in any meeting, nor to any group, had always been fearful of saying the wrong words, or of not being profound. But some irresistible force impelled me at last to add my voice in tribute. Recalling my youthful fears and sorrows, our visits to the sick together, the warm, sensible advice she gave, and her steadfastness in good times and bad, I blurted out the simple words which tried to tell what she had meant to me, yet not only to me:

"How many were the limbs she soothed, the hearts she touched? Her light shone strongly in the dark of fear and bigotry, lighting the way for countless others. She trod the narrow, crooked paths of righteousness firmly and joyfully; eagerly took upon her frail shoulders the heavy burdens of the Cross; and showed us all that faith is living, vibrant concern for others, answering to their needs. We needed wisdom and courage and understanding in our colony. Anne Hutchinson responded with such radiant love that lives everywhere in New England, yea, even in old England, are sweeter now and happier for her having dwelt among us. Truly she was a handmaiden of the Lord."

[*Eleventh month*]

Oh, how swiftly time does fly! Wee Anne creeps all about the house, hiding under tables, chairs, beds, and baskets, and pulls proudly to her feet clinging to my petticoats. I nearly spilt a kettle of stew upon her curly head the the other day, for she is continually under foot; but she is a dear, happy child, a joy to all of us.

Our big boy Sam trudges daily to the writing school held by the widow Smith, a private school, of course. Hornbook under his arm, ears and chin so swathed in scarves that only two bright eyes and little freckled nose peep out upon the frosty scene, he strides sturdily off to do battle with alphabet, sums,—and snowballs. His father misses him dreadfully and looks forward eagerly to springtime when Sam will again be trotting at his heels.

Mary, Willie, and Maher spend hours "mothering" their stocking dolls, stringing dried corn kernels or shaking them in a gourd, banging on a kettle, or chasing my yarn balls hither and yon. On dreary days Hope tells them stories and sings to them, and when all else fails, I let them help me—winding yarn, turning the spinning wheel, mixing the bread dough, or cooking some small treat. How odd it seems that I, an only child, should now have five babies, and that they should amuse themselves in many of the same ways that I did.

[*Sixth month, 1646*]

A most marvelous thing has happened: Susannah Hutchinson has been returned by the Indians! Ransomed by the Dutch, she is now with her older sisters in Boston. She is a wild, frightened little thing, we hear, who has forgotten both friends and native tongue, and indeed, she struggled desperately to remain with the savages. She is strong and sturdy (thank God) and will, I hope, respond quickly to the loving care of her family and forget the heathen life of the past three years (although she has been well treated by her captors). Why she was abducted at all is still a mystery—for hope of ransom? for her bright, shining hair and winsome face? or out of some grudging respect for her family's courage and nonresistance?

Sam Gorton, as staunchly independent as ever, has taken cordial leave of Portsmouth friends and, with his faithful followers, settled on the west bank of the river, below Providence at Shawomet. Having secured parliamentary permission to dwell in our plantations, he has chosen the mainland site as providing a bountiful, less strenuous existence, and perhaps also because it places more distance and obstacles between him and his Boston enemies.

Boston has recently made church attendance mandatory for all. Violators are to pay a five-shilling fine. Not everyone is allowed to join the church (and of course a nonmember may not hold public office), but everyone must attend for the good of his soul. How thankful Will and I are to have escaped this tyranny. It is a wonder to me how Captain Myles Standish of Plymouth with his Roman beliefs escaped persecution for so many years. Granted that his military experience and knowledge were most useful and that his fellow settlers were considerably more tolerant than their Puritan brothers, it still seems peculiar that this little red-haired soldier never felt the wrath of the Bay church. It is no secret that a few brash youths who referred to him audibly as "Captain Shrimpe" have felt the effects of his fiery temper.

The court has also decreed that when engagements are broken off unilaterally, the injured party is entitled to substantial monetary compensation. I suppose this came about because some men have gone to considerable expense to import a sweetheart from England, only to be deserted for a better prospect once she arrived.

Mr. Winthrop's fawning hangers-on, thinking the governor too august a personage to walk about like ordinary mortals, have presented him with a sedan chair—I suppose 'tis cheaper than paying off a mortgage for him!

[*Third month, 1647*]

The plantations' charter having finally become effective (with the capture of Charles and the strong hand of Cromwell and his Independents in Parliament), a general assembly convened this month in Portsmouth meetinghouse for residents of Providence, Shawomet, Portsmouth, Newport, Warwick, and outlying areas of our colony, to set up our permanent government and code of laws.

Our bill of rights, modeled after Magna Carta, provides for referenda, selection of assemblymen, power of veto, and collection of taxes by the towns, and court trials for criminal and some civil cases. Trial will be by a jury of twelve persons, with provision for defense counsel (unlike old England) and for appeal.

Our code of laws appears to be the most humane one extant today, based as it is on Christ's teachings rather than Moses'. Capital punishment is reserved for treason, murder, manslaughter, burglary, robbery, arson, and crimes against nature. While this is harsh enough, one must remember that in Massachusetts, Plymouth, and New Haven this same penalty is required also for heresy, blasphemy, cursing, or biting one's parents or not obeying them, being stubborn or rebellious, and similar "dangerous" crimes. Moreover, if any person here is so poor that he must steal to eat, he will not be punished. We do not condone the crime, but we recognize the occasional necessity for it. 'Tis the community that should be punished for not assisting the thief to find honest work.

Our code forbids witch trials—a poor woman was hanged recently in Windsor, Connecticut—, imprisonment for debts, banishment, and divorce for any reason but adultery. Although we have followed English law for the most part, we do not recognize primogeniture here, considering it unfair, undemocratic, and as working a great hardship on innocent persons. Witnesses in court may swear or not, as they choose; we shall try to discourage gossip by liberal use of the ducking stool; and for the general protection, all men aged seventeen through seventy are required to own and use bows and arrows.

No laws exist here pertaining to church establishment or attendance and membership. Jews, as well as Baptists, Congregationalists, and nonbelievers are welcome in our colony and public offices. No taxes or fees are collected for the clergy, and the latter are neither exempt from any of the laws, nor do they benefit more than anyone else from the laws. We are a God-fearing, God-loving community, but our church and government are separate.

Aquiday Island—1647

[*Eighth month*]

Our fourth son, Henry, named for our good friend, Harry Vane, lies sleeping in his cradle as I write. He is a precious thing, with fair hair and deep blue eyes, a round face, and plump little limbs. 'Tis a wonder he gets any sleep at all, the way the children hang over him. However, Hope has taken them for a walk along the Common, so Henry and I are both resting. Will was so pleased with his new son that he sent a barrel of ale round to the mill-and shipyard-workers, and dipped into it heartily himself—a little too heartily, I thought.

Massachusetts has provided by law for a system of free public education for her children. Every township of fifty householders is to have a reading or writing school, while towns of more than one hundred families are to have a grammar school also. Attendance is not compulsory, but it is thought that most parents will insist upon their children's going regularly. The young people simply cannot get ahead at anything but fishing or farming unless they have had some education. We really ought to do something more here for our children. Interest in education has decreased greatly since the schoolmaster left because of low pay, although of course there never was very much interest in it to begin with, or they would have paid him a decent wage. The majority of voters in the plantations are Baptists, and they seem to think it more important to prepare for the next life than for this one. I don't know what we shall do about Sam—he's already too old to continue at writing school, while Mary is of age now, and Willie soon will be. I suppose Will is right, a private school is the best answer. But at present we have no qualified and willing teacher for advanced study.

John Eliot of Massachusetts has learned the Algonquin

language so thoroughly, using Roger Williams' text, no doubt, that he is able to instruct the savages in religion, and has gone into the forest for that purpose. He is most successful with the little ones, rewarding them with cakes and apples for catechizing well—certainly a better teaching practice than beating them for their mistakes. Will stubbornly maintains that the hickory stick taught him all he knows, and that 'twill do a good job with his children, too. Furthermore, he growls, if Sam can't read any better by his birthday, he not only won't get the saddle he's been wanting for his pony, but he will get John Cotton's dull religious primer and spend his spare time reading it. However, Will is as big a fool as I am about these children, and he could no more whip any of them, or allow someone else to do so, than I could.

In spite of the general peace and prosperity now prevailing throughout the colony, I cannot help feeling somewhat apprehensive. Our good benefactor, Canonicus, died this summer. Long-lived for an Indian, he had reached the age of seventy. What his illness was we did not hear, but his dear friend Roger Williams was with him at the end to close his eyes and provide him a shroud. This wise, courteous, and greathearted chief befriended us all steadfastly through the years when lesser men cried for war. There is no one of his stature now to lead the tribe in peace, and I dread the prospect of a bloody uprising to decimate our homes and despoil our land.

Peter Stuyvesant has arrived to be governor of New Amsterdam. Pray God he may be more intelligent in his dealings with the Indians than his predecessor!

[*Fourth month, 1648*]

Will has ventured into the fishing business now—he just must have a finger in every pie, it seems. He has outfitted two vessels and hired crews to man them and occasionally even sails with them. He says he is devising ways of cutting the work and increasing the haul, but of course that is just an excuse for trying his hand with the line. He is also trying to design small, fast sloops for trade with Barbados and the Azores, but he has not yet achieved a plan which suits him.

Plymouth colony has finally built a meetinghouse—about time, after all the years of trudging up the hill to the fort. We have had one for some time now, but perhaps Newport has attracted more artisans than Plymouth, and certainly we are blessed with an abundance of wood; the climate is mild, the soil rich and smooth—it need not even be fertilized—, and life altogether easier for us than for the Plymouth settlers, whose fields are hilly and stony, and whose winters are bitterly cold.

The mood of depression which swept over us all in Boston during the winters seems still to prevail there and elsewhere, and has resulted in the hanging of two women recently for witchcraft. One was from Hartford, and the people make much of the fact that at the hour of her death a great storm arose and persisted for many hours. The other was Margaret Jones of Charlestown, whom we knew in Boston. A sober, godly woman of my own age, she was accused of causing sickness with her "malignant touch," and of foretelling the future. I shudder at her fate and fear for those others (for of course there must be others) as yet unknown, who will be dealt with in similar heartless, devilish fashion. The entire Bay colony and all the towns within its power lie under a suffocating blanket of evil and superstition, renewed continually by the unbalanced and malicious minds of her ministers, who worship a god of harshness and revenge, one who is relentless in his pursuit and punishment of the fallen. Oh, how thankful I am to breathe the pure, fresh air of Rhode Island's freedom!

However, the voice of contention, Will Coddington, still shatters the drowsy summer air, quarreling of this, that, and the other. Our president, with what view in mind we do not know, sought at a recent assembly to ally our colony with the United Colonies. Of course our independent and freedom-loving representatives shouted down the proposal, upon which C. broke into such a stream of epithets as has not been heard since we left Boston. Privately he has boasted to his intimates that he not only encouraged the Bay colony's harassing of Sam Gorton, but even provided them the information they needed to proceed! He further boasted that as president he is in an excellent position to inform them of our military and economic condition, and that he is very likely to do so if he is not given more power in our affairs. One or two of his cronies looked askance at these traitorous remarks and, fearing for the welfare of the plantations, related them to Will and Jeremy.

His chief complaints, however, are about religion, over which there has been much wrangling of late. "If a person be baptized once, he is baptized for all time, and any additional baptisms are nonsense!" he and his crony Partridge declare.

"On the contrary," say John Clarke, our physician and Anabaptist minister, and Nicholas Easton, our sawmill owner and assistant, "an individual baptized in one faith must be rebaptized when he joins another faith, for he is being born again and cleansed of sins permitted by the old faith. Parents who baptize their infants shortly after birth do not assure them of salvation, for baptism is for believers, and what can an infant believe, or say that he believes? Nay, a child must be old enough to comprehend doctrine before he can believe it and accept it through baptism."

"By what authority do you say these things?" demands Mr. Coddington testily. "I don't recall reading them in the Book!"

"Ah," replies John tranquilly, "we are inspired directly by God. We cherish the Bible but acknowledge the spirit of it—not the letter—together with personal revelation as our most trustworthy guide to living."

At this Mr. C. falls silent, for these words are reminiscent of Anne Hutchinson, whom he staunchly defended many years ago.

As if this weren't enough, personal relations between our families have worsened of late, partly because we Dyers now worship with John Clarke's congregation, partly because of other exasperating incidents which came to a climax recently and caused serious repercussions.

If only Mr. C. had kept his fences mended! It had nothing to do with politics, seemingly; but when Will rode out last week to our farm and found Mr. C.'s cattle trampling the flax and gobbling the wheat, he stormed into town and confronted Mr. C. with a demand for damages.

"Damages indeed, Will Dyer!" Coddington snapped. "Do you think you can exact payment from the president of the plantations? Besides," he sneered, "what of the ten head of cattle you took from my farm and are still milking? What of that, Sir?"

Will was speechless at this blatantly false accusation, but only for a moment. Then he exploded. "By thunder, I'll 'president' thee!" he roared, clutching Mr. C.'s lapels and shaking him violently. "I've never milked any of thy confounded, blundering cows yet, but by heaven, I'll milk every last one if they're not off my land by sundown.

And furthermore, Mr. President of the plantations, we'll just see how long thou'lt remain in thy mighty office after the assembly charges thee with treason!" With that he stamped off, flinging Mr. C. from him as he would a rat in the grist mill.

Within a few days a special assembly convened. Although the charges were reduced to "giving countenance, information, and comfort to Massachusetts" (through his correspondence with Governor Winthrop), and thus should have brought only a moderate penalty at most, the fact that Mr. C. did not appear to defend himself caused an adverse reaction, and both he and Mr. Baulston were suspended. Assistant Easton was then named president.

So we enjoy now an uneasy peace. Mr. C., proud man that he is, has taken this blow ill indeed. Shutting himself off from all but close friends, he has retired to his house at the cove with his widowed daughter. The cows have been pastured farther away, and occasionally his lonely figure is discerned from afar, supervising the removal of rocks from the soil to their place in what will be, let us hope, a firm boundary wall.

[*Eighth month*]

It now appears that Mr. C.'s treachery was greater than any of us suspected. While supposedly repenting his sins at Rocky Farm, he was, on the contrary, plotting secretly to further his insatiable ambitions; for he and his minions put us in grave danger of losing our treasured freedom. Falsely declaring that they had the consent of the majority, they last month petitioned the Boston-controlled United Colonies to receive Rhode Island as a member. Fortunately our few friends in the group were successful in denying the petition. But the remarkable thing is that as long ago as 1644 Mr. C. had initiated secret correspondence concerning our membership! It is just incredible that he could have acted like this.

As soon as the attempt became known here, Mr. C. and his daughter fled to Boston. Rumors have reached us that they plan to sail for England in the spring, apply to Parliament for recognition of him as proprietor of Aquidneck, and ask that he be appointed governor! Really, he seems obsessed with a desire for power, and the devious and crafty methods in a man formerly honest and forthright bespeak some unhingement of the mind. Bedaiah Coddington and his wife remain to attend to his father's affairs.

1649-1651

[*Third month, 1649*]

Mother writes that England is still in political upheaval. Last Tenth month the Cromwellian Colonel Pride burst in upon Parliament with his men and arrested all those members, mostly Presbyterians, who had voted to return Charles to the throne. Harry Vane and one or two other high-principled men, appalled at this interference by the military, resigned at once in vehement protest. The remaining members continued to sit as a "rump" parliament, speedily brought the king to trial from the Isle of Wight, and had him executed, all within two months' time —a record for any parliamentary action. He met his death bravely without whimper or complaint, according to Mother's London friends. Next month Cromwell installed a council of state to govern the country along with the parliamentary remnant until a new ruler can be chosen. Harry Vane was appointed a member of this council.

Here at home a real pirate sailed into harbor one day and rowed ashore with some of his vile cutthroats. Bluefield's French accent and raucous laugh resounded through the town, causing most of the men and boys to desert their hammers and saws to hear him boast of his bloody deeds. Will and Sam were the biggest fools of all, following at his heels all morning as he swaggered about town, buying the captured ship he offered for sale, and waving good-bye as he and his crew pulled away in their longboat. If the more sober townsmen had not restrained Will, he would gladly have sold this evil rogue a fast sloop, the better to rob our own ships!

"Ah, 'tis a glorious life, the life of a pirate!" exclaimed Will at supper that evening. "Plenty of fresh salt air and wind—no stuffy mills or shops—adventure, excitement, and riches, much more than one could ever make on land."

"Indeed?" I retorted. "And what is wrong with the salt air at the shipyard?"

"Pah! 'Tis fouled by all the pitch we use."

I tried a new tack. "Excitement and adventure! What are they to thee at thy age? With six children to care for wouldst thou be sailing off for months at a time, risking thy life to murder and plunder people who have never harmed thee? And do gulping wormy biscuit and being soaked to the skin appeal so much to thee that thou wouldst leave this good stew and warm hearth? As for riches, thou art already one of the wealthiest men here. Don't be a fool, Will. Pirating is a dirty, disgraceful life and well dost thou know it!"

At this tirade Will and Sam sat glumly silent, and the subject was not mentioned again. However, I feel rather uneasy about the matter, for at times there is a faraway look in Will's eyes, and he actually seems to be daydreaming.

From Boston comes word of the death of John Winthrop. When Will expressed his regret and his admiration of Mr. W.'s "great qualities of justice, wisdom, and courage," I could not help snapping that he had not always admired the gentleman so unrestrainedly. Really, I don't know what to make of Will these days.

The Coddingtons have indeed sailed for England, with what plans we cannot be sure. The assembly did discuss the possibility of Mr. C.'s causing trouble, but no action was taken.

[*Third month, 1650*]

Two of Jane Hawkins' boys living in Boston have petitioned that she be permitted to return there. They not only promised to provide for her so that she would not become a public charge but also declared she would not be allowed to "doctor" or to gossip. Boston, however, still mindful of her past misdeeds, summarily denied the petition. Thus she remains at Portsmouth with young Tom and his wife and children. My, it doesn't seem possible that her boys are all married now with boys of their own.

[*Seventh month*]

Mother writes that Will and Mary Coddington are busily visiting and entertaining all the influential officials they can scrape up an acquaintance with. It is no secret there that he is mustering support for the time when he petitions the council of state for a grant of our island. Mother says he saw Harry Vane and was cordial to him but did not disclose his plans, knowing how friendly to us Harry is. However, he was not so reticent with Mr. Hugh Peter; indeed, quite the opposite. They have become real cronies, for Mr. Peter has much influence in London now, as he preaches at Whitehall before the council and ministry.

Numerous meetings have been held throughout the plantations to discuss what we shall do if Mr. C. succeeds, but still there are no definite plans. Obviously any such grant would be illegal according to our patent of 1644, but the council may void all royal patents now that there is no king. Our men must be cautious, as they cannot risk the consequences of outright rebellion against the Commonwealth.

[*Third month, 1651*]

Mother writes that the council has referred Coddington's petition to the commission of the admiralty, and they will make their decision shortly. There is even a possibility that if *he* is denied the grant, it will go to Plymouth, for their Mr. Winslow also has claimed our land! Truly, we are beset on every side.

Will has given up plans to send Sam on to college. We have no proper grammar school here, as everyone is too busy bickering about religion to spare any time or energy on a mere secular school. So Will is instructing the boy now in astronomy, mathematics, geography, and sailing, thus fitting him for a sea life. Sam enjoys it all immensely, but I could have wished for a safer profession on dry land.

Mary has replaced Hope as my "assistant" and is a scrupulous housekeeper and baby nurse. Hope married a young farmer this spring. Willie is a real blessing, for he cheerfully performs the chores, which Will and Sam have abandoned, before he skips off to school in the morning and after he dashes home in the afternoon. Farm life suits him fine. "Sam can have his calms and storms and torn sails and sharks," he scoffs. "I'll take cows and horses and growing things anytime!"

[*Fourth month*]

Coddington has won! The shocking news was cried in the streets not one hour ago. "Hear ye! Hear ye, one and all!" the crier boomed, calling us all from house and shop. When a small crowd had gathered, he read the proclamation: " 'Know you, all people of Providence Plantations, that by the authority of the Commonwealth of England we do acknowledge and affirm the petition of William Coddington concerning the Isle of Aquidneck and Isle of Conanicut, and do appoint him governor of these islands, and do command your faithful obedience to all his orders. Signed, John Bradshaw, Committee of the Admiralty.' " Then he moved on to other streets, returning later to nail the paper upon our meetinghouse door.

The assemblymen and other officials are now hastening to Portsmouth for another informal meeting. I pray they will find some way to avoid this separation and despotism.

[*Fifth month*]

The meeting was sadly concluded. They had no recourse but to honor the Commonwealth's order, and to sever all political ties with Aquidneck. We continue with them, however, in a common desire for future unity and with an unwritten agreement to work together for the common defense.

Although we bemoan this grievous turn of events, we are not despondent. John Clarke has offered to meet Mr. Coddington—I cannot call him Governor—when he docks at Boston and attempt to dissuade him from his selfish and calamitous path. If this measure fails, we still have recourse to all our friends in England—Harry, Admiral Penn, and the many English Dyers. They will certainly give us freely of their time, energy, talents, and money for this noble cause.

Aquiday Island—1651

[*Sixth month*]

Our dear John Clarke, gentle, patient, wise, devout, who never harmed a soul in his life, who never even raised his voice against anyone, returned to Newport today bewildered and sickened by the violence and cruelty which masquerade as religion in Boston. As a man of strong character, influence, and authority, as a Newport assistant, physician, and minister, he had felt no misgivings about journeying into the lion's den. How sadly he was mistaken!

Taking with him two members of his church, John Crandall of Newport, Sam Gorton's son-in-law, and Obadaiah Holmes, formerly a Baptist minister at Seekonk, he rode first to Swampscott, a village near Lynn. This is his account as given on Newport common:

"We set out on a mission of mercy. My friend, William Witter, admonished by Boston court five years ago for decrying the practice of infant baptism, is now an old man, widowed, blind, sick, helpless, shunned by his neighbors, a piteous wretch dying alone. 'Twas our church which sent us to comfort him, and so in the fresh, sweet air under the leafy boughs I preached to him on how to be patient amid his temptations. For he was sorely tempted: tempted to deny God's love and justice, to revile his neighbors, to despair.

"And while we were worshiping quietly there, two constables rudely plunged from the thicket into our midst. 'We have warrants for your arrest,' they snapped. 'First, because you are strangers, and second, because your opinions do not coincide with our teachings.' With that they hustled us roughly to the ale house at Lynn, leaving poor William Witter dazed and alone.

"Next day the constables herded us to Boston for

trial. After two weeks' confinement and little food but still in good spirits, we were brought before the court, Major Endecott presiding. Although he had been so rash as to cut the cross from the town ensign and speak against the king while in Salem, the moment he began to breathe the stifling air of the Bay colony he became more conservative and rigid than any of the other Bostonians. With the help of the ministers he questioned us minutely about our religious beliefs and 'erroneous opinions.'

" 'My dear Sir!' I exclaimed indignantly at one point. 'Who are you—or the court—to say what religious opinions are mistaken or true? Only God in heaven can determine that.'

" 'Silence!' he thundered. 'You and your notions are naught but trash and deserve only the utmost contempt from all decent citizens. Nay more, death would not be too harsh a punishment. Nevertheless I shall be glad to engage you in debate before the ministers at some other time.'

"At this your old friend John Cotton, somewhat alarmed, arose and spoke. His cheeks are still ruddy and his dress and bearing bespeak his high social position, together with a well-filled purse and stomach.

" 'Speaking for the ministers,' he said pompously, 'although we are grateful for the invitation to hear the thoughts of your keen and erudite mind, do you not consider that such a debate will expose lesser and weaker minds to the possibility of seduction? Rather than airing these foolish views even among our own learned clergy, we must shut them up tightly and see that they taint no one here.'

" 'Yes, yes, you are right, Mr. Cotton,' the governor agreed. 'Now, as to the verdict. . . .' He glanced around the room, and heads nodded solemnly. 'The court finds you three guilty.'

" 'But what law have we broken?' I cried. 'We are strangers and do apologize sincerely if we have unwittingly transgressed. But surely we are entitled to know *how* we have transgressed.'

"However, Endecott merely scowled and muttered, 'We know the law.' Then he continued, 'The sentence will be. . . .' Here he was interrupted by Mr. Cotton.

" 'If the court please, Sir, the defendant Crandall holds no public office or position of influence and may therefore receive a light fine. The other two, however, being ministers and holding great sway over many minds, must be punished in accordance with their ability and opportunity to infect others with these false and evil opinions. Let their punishment be both severe fines and whipping.'

" 'Governor! Governor!' cried a layman. 'This would be folly! To whip a man of John Clarke's political stature would bring the wrath of Providence Plantations upon us, resulting in cessation of the trade and commerce which we badly need. Mr. Holmes, too, has friends who can lighten our purses. Let us not be rash about this matter.'

" 'Besides,' a naïve voice spoke up, 'fines and whipping are illegal in this case. Banishment is the only sentence meted to Anabaptists.'

" 'Nonsense!' cried John Wilson. 'Nothing is too severe for these incendiaries. They must be hounded from the land.'

"When quiet had been restored, Governor Endecott read out the sentence: 'You three shall be fined in the following amounts and then banished from our jurisdiction. John Crandall, £5; John Clarke, £20; Obadaiah Holmes, £30. Failure to pay the fine will result in one lash for each pound not paid. Can you pay?' His eyes glittered expectantly.

"We looked at one another aghast, for we carried little money with us and indeed would have been hard put to raise such enormous sums readily at home. However, old friends came to my rescue, and the gaoler, a secret admirer of Sam Gorton, paid John's fine. But Obadaiah, in spite of his advanced age, refused to accept aid.

" 'I bless God that I am counted worthy to suffer for the name of Jesus,' he said humbly.

"Hearing this, Mr. Wilson sprang up in a rage. 'The curse of God go with thee!' he screeched, and struck Obadaiah full in the face.

"Our friend stumbled backward but offered no violence in return and only gazed sorrowfully at the minister, who was restrained with difficulty from a further assault, until we were escorted to gaol again. He slept soundly that night, while John and I prayed.

"Next day, carrying his Testament, he walked firmly with us to the common, allowed himself to be stripped to the waist and his wrists bound to the post. He gazed placidly over the great crowd, picking out a friend here, a persecutor there; but Governor Endecott, who had tried, judged, and sentenced him, could not bear the sight of the blood to be shed and remained at home.

"Then the executioner picked up his lash of three cords, spat on his hands, and began. Obadaiah's body seemed to take on the resignation and relaxation of his mind, for he neither winced nor moaned. And when it was finally over and we hurried to free him, we were further astonished by the joy and love radiating from his countenance. Turning to the executioner he said kindly, 'You have struck me as with roses.' The man gaped in amazement, and a gleam of admiration leaped to his eyes.

"Thus did this brave servant of the Lord confound his tormentors. Cruel men that they were, they allowed us no time to bind his raw and bleeding back but hurried us from their boundaries. Safe at last, we passed several days resting in the forest, poor Obadaiah crouching on hands and knees to ease the pain. When I was sure that his wounds would heal properly, I left him in John's devoted care and rushed to warn you, my dear friends, of the dangers which beset us all."

So he concluded his tale of shocking savagery pitted against sublime faith. Horrified and indignant, we buzzed angrily of retribution: a blockade of ships, denial of our roads to their travelers, a committee of protest, a petition to Parliament, and so on.

The steady clop-clop of a horse's hooves diverted our attention to the street, and it was with a common revulsion that we observed the arrival of Will Coddington. Sitting stiffly astride his fine gray mount, an insolent smile on his haughty face, he advanced slowly to the common. Impassively we watched him come, yet we all felt the antagonism which lay heavy on the air.

Even he appeared to sense it. "Is this the proper way to welcome your governor?" he inquired coldly.

There was a moment of silence. "I'll welcome thee properly indeed, Governor Traitor!" cried my Will then, springing forward. He seized the horse's reins and would have toppled C. from his saddle, but a sudden cut of the whip loosened Will's grasp. The governor wheeled sharply and fled in ignominious haste, clinging to his horse's neck.

We burst into laughter, and several small boys ran after him, hooting and jeering. Even Will could not help smiling, but he sobered quickly. Calling John Clarke and several other prominent men aside, he argued earnestly for prompt action against both Boston and the governor.

At last they agreed: John Clarke will seek Parliament's

aid in halting religious persecution in the Bay colony, and Will is to accompany him as private secretary. Furthermore, Roger Williams will be asked to sail with us and press for revocation of Coddington's commission. We leave immediately the harvest is accomplished.

It is all settled, and there is a certain relief and joy in knowing that we have determined on a course and will pursue it to the end. Certainly we shall prevail, for justice and right are on our side. In time, not only shall Providence Plantations be once more united, but all people throughout the New World shall worship openly as they please, and fear and oppression shall be banished from our land.

[*Eighth month*]

Our fiercely independent Islanders have risen up in wrath and rebelled against attempted tyranny. Bursting into Mr. C.'s town house, where he was holding court, Captain Richard Morris and his men ordered the meeting to disperse, saying it was not a legally constituted court. Next day the governor rashly sent his Captain Partridge to the common to read a proclamation commanding order and obedience. This so incensed the people that they began to riot, pummeling the captain and his men, hurling stones, breaking windows, and otherwise expressing their disapproval. The governor next sent his personal messenger racing to John Winthrop, Jr., for aid, but as this young man was not disposed to become embroiled, and as a stone whizzed past Mr. C.'s nose every time he poked it out the door, the governor shortly consigned his proclamation to the flames, snatched up a few belongings, and fled in the night to the hard, cold bosom of Boston for the winter. He was luckier than Captain Partridge, who failed to escape and lost his life at the end of a rope.

Will has mortgaged our holdings here to provide ready funds for all expenses. We leave for England this day week. Mr. Williams has already gone.

Glastonbury
[*Tenth month*] *England*

England, England, England! How my limbs trembled as we neared Southampton's shore and I perceived again the shops and dwellings, the cobbled streets, which were so long ago my last glimpse of this beloved homeland. How my eyes devoured every tree and every bush, every cottage, every stone throughout the bleak and chilly countryside; and how my ears strained to catch the plaintive cheep of hungry sparrows, shutting out the clamor of the children as they played and bickered in the coach. What inexpressible joy to tread again the halls at Glastonbury and to enfold once more my darling Mother in my eager arms! The years of painful separation and of sorrow have melted away like the snows of spring and I am content and happy, for I have come home.

1652-1653

[*First month, 1652*]

Mother is really in her element, although she still appears dazed at times over this sudden wealth of flesh-and-blood grandchildren. They whoop and clatter through the halls, knock over the furniture, and spill their ale at table, but with never a word of rebuke from their grandmother. How different it was when I was a child! Outside they nimbly climb the historic granite tor where bloomed our famous thorn tree (sprung from Joseph of Arimathaea's staff) till overzealous Puritans cut it down; explore the ancient ruined abbey founded by Joseph and housing the bones of Arthur and Guinevere; scamper among the great timbers of the fallen tithing barn where tithes of grain were stored; and noisily slake their thirst at the Blood Spring where Joseph is said to have hidden the sacred chalice used at the Last Supper.

We took the older children recently to London, showing them Westminster Abbey and Hall, the palace, the Tower, and of course the house where we once lived. The children were struck dumb by the city's immense size and crowded streets, the massive churches, close-set shops and houses, the fog and soot, the ragged, sniffling youngsters begging in the gutter, the vendors hawking their wares, and the roaming packs of hungry dogs.

Visiting the Vanes at their town house, we found Harry's wife to be a lovely, charming hostess, who has furnished the place simply yet beautifully, in keeping with their aversion to extravagance and display.

The Penns, however, had gleaming silver and shining silks in profusion, much to the children's awe; but we were warmly welcomed, and all soon felt at ease. The admiral, with his own little Will in tow and a youthful spring in his step, one day rowed the children out to a warship. They peered into the cannon, scampered along the decks, explored the cabins and hold, tried to climb the ratlines (thereby incurring several bumps and bruises), got into everyone's way, and thought it all great fun.

Leaving Will and Sam to take rooms with John Clarke and Roger Williams in the city, we started our return journey, digressing from our route to visit the Roman ruins and warm springs at Bath. An attendant at the baths permitted the children to try an ancient skinscraper he had found nearby; they agreed heartily that they preferred soap! The baths are again becoming popular and the town is a resort for people who use its mineral waters for all sorts of ailments, including indigestion, rheumatism, skin diseases, wounds, and gout. Promising the children another visit in warmer weather, I shooed them back to the coach and we resumed our journey, arriving home safely, tired but happy.

[*Sixth month*]

Will writes that Harry Vane is now president of the Council of State, so we may hope for more sympathetic treatment of our problems. Mr. C.'s agent is in London, but Harry has refused to see him.

Will sent us copies of John Clarke's account of his own sufferings and those of other Anabaptists. He says that John's tracts are selling well, and there is much talk in Parliament of taking action. But I suppose they will follow their usual course and debate until the need for action is past.

Will has also written concerning a new religious sect, the "Children of Light," or, as sometimes called, "Quakers." Believing in simplicity of dress, they lit a great fire at Malton recently and cast on it all their bright ribbons and bows, shiny silks, gowns, and doublets, and now clothe themselves only in plain, dark garments. He says they meet in fields or houses without a minister or priest. Sometimes they sit in silence; then again several people may talk or pray, as they are moved to do so. (This sounds much like some of our services at Portsmouth and Newport.) Occasionally the entire group is afflicted with quaking and trembling. (No doubt they speak in tongues, too, Will sneers.) They even believe women have souls and let them speak in their meetings! One Elizabeth Hooton, a middle-aged itinerant, not only preaches but also rebukes the clergy openly and vigorously, and for this she has been several times in gaol. A former servant girl, Mary Fisher, is now a zealous "quaker and reprover," and often in gaol.

The tales about their leader, George Fox, are also varied. He is said to have been converted by the Voice of the Lord (I remember Anne's Voice); to wear a broad-brimmed white hat and leather suit of his own making; to believe that God plants a divine seed in the heart of every person, a seed which one may nourish or neglect. He rejects all outward forms of religion, all the church's traditions and most of her doctrines including the sacraments; all paid ministers and prepared sermons; all extravagance, waste, luxury, vanity, changes in fashion; slavery, war, military service, violence, taxes to support church and army; oaths, capital punishment for petty crimes, imprisonment for debt, and heaven knows what else! He walks or rides horseback from village to town, speaking in the churches after meeting, or on the hillsides. One of John Cotton's former students, now ministering an independent church in this country, earnestly tells his people that George Fox rides a big, black horse which can run sixty miles in one minute; and that he carries with him magic bottles to bewitch the people into following him! Other people argue vigorously that he is an angel come to earth or another John the Baptist.

Will and I are to visit the Vanes this fall at their country home in Lincolnshire, and it is my fond hope then to see and hear George Fox in person. Will scoffs at many of the Quaker beliefs, but I feel they are certainly no more nonsensical than his applying for a privateer's license. Really, I don't know what has come over him. 'Tis all the fault of that dreadful pirate Bluefield, and if I could only lay hands on him, I would cheerfully wring his neck!

[*Ninth month*] *Lincolnshire*

How thrilling it is to be here in the region where Anne Hutchinson grew up and married. We have visited St. Botolph's town, now called Boston, where she lived as a girl, and worshiped at St. Botolph's Church, where her father was pastor. This lovely church is a landmark for miles around, its tall gray tower piercing the heavens by day, its lantern guiding the traveler by night. The clear clock bells count each hour, summoning the people to work in the early morning and to rest in the late evening.

The dark, fluted, oaken pulpit where Pastor Marbury (and John Cotton, too,) preached still holds his thick, worn Bible; the pews are scratched and scuffed. Nearby the brick-and-timber manse, with its glinting panes and smoking chimneys, peeps out from a fruitful orchard. How Anne must have enjoyed playing here as a child, climbing among the branches, breathing in the sweet scent of blossoms! We visited also the Guildhall basement and those dark, cold cells where William Brewster and William Bradford lay imprisoned after their first attempt to flee the country.

A few days later we rode to Alford, the village where Anne lived after her marriage. Here too we saw the house she and Will lived in, the streets they walked. We even talked lovingly of them with people they had known—but not so lovingly of Will Coddington, whose home this also was.

Poor Mr. Coddington! Through Harry's tireless efforts his commission has been revoked, and once more our dear plantations will be reunited. But his troubles are not over, for we hear he is suspected of conspiring with the Dutch! Will is to leave with the news as soon as the weather moderates, probably next month, but I shall remain with Mother for a few months longer. Roger Williams and the Clarkes also will stay, to keep a sharp eye on our affairs. Sam and Mary will go with Will, for he cannot part from his firstborn, and Mary must look after them. Willie and Maher will go to school in Glastonbury, and Mother will continue to spoil the youngest ones.

[*Tenth month*] *Glastonbury*

Mary, Sam, and Will have gone. My heart grieved to see them go, especially my dear husband, for we had quarreled bitterly. It began in Holland, Lincolnshire, where we rested one sabbath on our return journey. In the morning as we were preparing to attend the village church, we noticed a number of people entering a nearby house. Their hats bore no feathers or ribbons, their coats and gowns neither laces nor bows.

"Look, Will!" I cried. "They must be Quakers going to worship. Do let us go in. I shan't rest until I've attended one of their meetings."

He agreed reluctantly, and reminding the children to be quiet we joined the group. Most were seated on benches in the large room, but some were standing. Several people moved over to make room for us. For a time everyone was silent. Then a woman rose, untied her bonnet, and knelt upon the clean, bare floor. When everyone had risen quietly and the men removed their hats, she began to pray. Her voice was hardly audible, her words simple. Hers was not the effortless flow of the practiced speaker. Rather, each thought seemed to force itself from her lips after a long pause.

"God of love, who art love, and who raineth love upon all thy children, . . . open our hearts that we may love in equal measure. . . . Nourish the seed that is within us that we may forget the little troubles of this life and dwell upon the everlasting things. . . . Open our ears to thy voice, give speech to our mouths, strengthen our feeble spirits and unwilling limbs. . . . Lead us by the hand, O Lord, for injury, scorn, and death are naught if only thou art close."

After a few more moments, apparently lacking further inspiration, she resumed her seat, and we seated ourselves also. Again there was a silence which grew deeper and deeper, it seemed to me as I pondered her words, until even the rumbling and creaking of an occasional cart outside was stilled.

Then a male voice began, softly and hesitantly at first, but growing more confident until the words gushed from his mouth. He told of the prosperous business he once had and the fears which consumed him because of it; of his loving family and how his love stifled both them and him. Finally he told us that by giving up business and family, by witnessing for God in the streets in spite of rain and cold, jeers and stones, he had become joyful rather than fearful, for he had personally felt God's hand assisting him time after time; his family too had benefited from divine Providence, for kind neighbors fed, clothed, and sheltered them and found work for his wife. Therefore he was convinced that if one preached God's Word and followed Christ's example, both one's physical and spiritual needs would somehow be met. His face beamed with confidence and love, and I could not help contrasting his teachings, spirit, and demeanor with those of the Boston ministers. Surely a just and loving Father spoke through this good man, poor and uneducated though he was.

As he urged us finally in his sweet, ringing voice to flee worldly temptations and possessions and to devote ourselves wholly to God, I felt my scalp tingle. Chills raced up my spine, and my brain reeled. I felt about me a like response of other hearts and minds. Emotion pressed upon us, ecstatic joy enveloped us. It was too much—I felt I must cry out. But slowly the spirit ebbed away, and in a few moments people began to rise. A friendly hand clasped mine, a warm voice bade me welcome. All around, people were smiling and talking happily with what could only be the light of love beaming from their faces. I answered friendly queries as in a dream; and only recovered my senses when I heard Will speak to one of the men.

"Who are they who spoke?"

And the man replied simply, "Elizabeth Hooton and William Dewsbury."

My heart pounded anew. These two were renowned far and wide among Quakers for their fervor and zeal, their courage and forthrightness. Yet here they spoke in humility and simplicity with far greater effect than any minister I had ever heard.

Outside Will hustled us all into the inn.

"What a marvelous experience!" I exclaimed breathlessly. "And what wonderful people those two are!"

"Oh, come," growled Will, "what is so wonderful abcut a man who will leave his family to starve while he roams the country? And what about his shop? Profitable businesses don't grow on trees."

"But Will, he said his family didn't suffer."

"No thanks to him."

"Besides, he was called to preach. Surely one cannot ignore a call from God, Will."

"No, of course not. All I'm saying is that he ought to have provided for his family first."

"But wouldn't that indicate a lack of faith in the Lord?"

"First Timothy: 'If any provide not for his own, and specially for those of his own house, he hath denied the faith, and is worse than an infidel,' " he quoted angrily.

"Matthew," I replied just as heatedly: " 'Behold the fowls of the air; for they sow not, neither do they reap, nor gather into barns; yet your heavenly Father feedeth them,' " but Will had turned his back stubbornly and was scolding the poor children, who, never having heard us quarrel before, now sat with mouths agape.

Although Will soon regained his usual good humor and

we conversed pleasantly on other topics, my heart ached at the lack of understanding between us on what seemed to me a vital point. The rift widened when we reached home. Lying on the hall table was a parliamentary commission naming Will commander-in-chief of any and all privateers in the plantations, and awarding him the rank of captain! I glowered as Will let out a piercing whoop and pranced up and down the hall with Sam. If he were fifty years younger, I thought bitterly, he'd be turning handsprings.

Noticing my displeasure he stopped abruptly and, taking my hands in his, said softly, "Dearest Mary, a privateer isn't really the same as a pirate—he's much more respectable. He has a license to stop other ships and take their supplies."

"Aye, a license to steal!" I cried.

"It isn't stealing when it's for a man's country!"

"Stealing is stealing, no matter for what reason. And killing—I suppose killing innocent, harmless strangers isn't really killing either?"

"But it's different when one's at war," he protested. "Besides, they're not innocent and harmless. They're guilty of aiding the enemy."

"Don't quibble, Will. There may be some justification for fighting in one's own defense—although I'm not even sure about that—but deliberately to attack another, seize his private property, and perhaps kill him, is certainly wrong."

"Mary," he replied, squaring his shoulders stubbornly, "it's our patriotic duty to harass the Dutch any way we can. Our country not only sanctions but commands it."

"Then I hope thou'lt be very happy as a patriotic thief and murderer!" I wailed, and fled in tears to my room.

Will, Sam, and Mary left next day; and as we bade one another Godspeed, Will and I both realized that the broad

Atlantic is not wider than the great gulf which already separates us.

[*Third month, 1653*]

A short letter from Will informs us that Mr. Coddington quietly accepted the revocation of his commission. He has signed over the deed, except for his own personal holdings, to the rest of the islanders and, assured that no one now intends him bodily harm, has returned to Newport.

Will makes no mention of any privateering, but a note from Mary indicates he and Sam are harassing our own ships more than the enemies'! What can the colony be thinking of to entrust its safety to a miller? And to Captain Underhill, also commissioned a privateer, who knows little enough about fighting on land—although he is adept at parading in uniform—and still less about fighting on the sea. Mary wrote that they had stayed overnight in Boston with Anne Hutchinson's son, Captain Edward, and that Sam was much smitten with granddaughter Anne's charms. Little Susannah, now an attractive young lady, has forgotten her years with the Indians and was married shortly after we left for England to John Cole of Boston. It hardly seems possible that she has started a family and that our own Sam should be thinking of doing so, too.

Margaret Fell, the daughter of an old friend of Mother's and an ardent Quaker, has invited me to visit at her home in Ulverston and learn firsthand about this sect. I shall leave as soon as Charlie recovers from his cold.

Swarthmore Hall
[*Fifth month*] *Ulverston*

Margaret Fell is truly a good and great woman. She has taken me warmly into her house and heart as she has taken so many others, and imparted to my eager ears the simple faith and practice of the Friends (as Quakers prefer to be called). Converted last year upon hearing George Fox, she has fed and sheltered all passing Friends, sent them money, and penned countless letters to her own relations and acquaintances, begging their assistance also. Her husband, the judge, while remaining a staunch churchman, nevertheless is so devoted to Margaret that he willingly acquiesces in all her endeavors. He is often away on duty and frequently returns to find the house filled with strangers; but he is always cordial and pleasant.

George Fox has been here a week or two, recovering from his latest prison ordeal. Although his spirit has remained strong, his iron constitution has suffered somewhat, for conditions in the gaols are abominable. Prisoners are crowded into cold, drafty cells with only a bit of straw to lie on—if there is room to lie at all. The floors are damp and filthy as there is no waste disposal. Concerned friends bring food and clothing, but these items do not always reach the prisoners. Few of the Quakers despair, however; indeed, they look upon gaol sentences as heaven-sent opportunities to serve the Lord. As George Fox said to me humbly and reverently, "*I was never in prison but it was the means of bringing multitudes out of their prisons.*" Friends do seem to thrive under persecution, for their numbers increase daily.

What an exceptional man is their leader! His piercing brown eyes seemed actually to scrutinize my soul when first we met; his plain, sober face, with its long, sharp nose, heavy brows, and round chin, radiated love; and though he seldom smiled, children flocked about him, for he always had time to joggle them gently on his knee. I also saw him one day enfold in his arms a small dog, which had been viciously kicked by one of the servants. "These, too, are God's creation, my friend," he chided, "to be cherished even as our Father cherishes us." But the man only scowled as if he would kick God, too, if he got in his way! So George Fox does not reach every heart.

The evening George spoke to a group of new Friends concerning his conversion will always be one of the most memorable of my life. Sitting before the fire in his broad-brimmed hat and leather suit, he told first of the years he had spent as a troubled youth traveling the countryside 'round his home, studying and asking questions of ministers, laymen, the educated and uneducated: Why was there such extravagance of dress when Christ wore only a simple robe? Why did men waste their time and substance at drinking and playing cards? Why should studying at Oxford or Cambridge fit a man to be a minister of Christ, when the apostle said believers needed no man to teach them? Should not every Christian be a minister unto others as he occupies himself at some trade, even as did Jesus and the ignorant fishermen?

Despondent at not finding any satisfactory answers, he turned to solitude and nature, and one day heard a voice proclaiming, "There is one, even Christ Jesus, that can speak to thy condition." He saw also what he called an ocean of darkness and death, and over it an infinite ocean of light and love, which was the infinite love of God.

He then went on to tell how he was able to reveal new interpretations of the Scriptures and speak forcefully of the old ones to great numbers of people. About this time a local prophet, although dying, declared that George was an instrument of the Lord and would accomplish much for him. After the man's death, George fell into a divine stupor having the appearance of death and lay inactive for two weeks; then he arose, quite changed in appearance and renewed in spirit. He said he was led through the "ocean of darkness" and delivered from Satan, Sodom, Babylon, Egypt, and the grave by a vision of God's infinite love. People talked of it for weeks.

Then, George said, he understood that the light of Christ was in all men to guide them to a richer life; and those that followed the inward light he called children of the light. It was his mission, he said, to turn people from the darkness to this light and to lead them to the Holy Spirit and thence to truth, grace, and salvation. George has ranged far and wide, urging the people to free themselves from the church's harsh and rigid rule and find salvation in the love and service of Jesus by living as simply, as kindly, and as singlemindedly as he did. Truly this is a great man.

[*Sixth month*]

Mother writes that Harry Vane has once more been returned to private life. Pressing always for greater tolerance and liberty, he last spring introduced a bill which would allow people of all religious faiths to vote, and would safeguard the people from despotic wickedness and oppression. But Puritan Cromwell was unable to bear the thought of Roman Catholics, Ranters, Seekers, Quakers, etc., having a hand in the government. He directed his supporters to prevent passage of the bill. When they failed to bring it to a satisfactory vote, he himself took a hand.

Wearing his customary plain black suit and gray worsted stockings, he appeared one day in the House and demanded that the question be put. A chorus of "ayes" approved the bill. Cromwell's face reddened fearfully. He brought all guns to bear and let loose a vitriolic fusillade of abuse upon the members as they sat in silent amazement at this unprecedented interference. Catching his breath, he bellowed for the guard.

"Out!" he roared. "I declare this incompetent, irresponsible body dissolved! Out, I say!"

Harry sprang to his feet. "Stop!" he cried. "This proceeding is illegal!"

Cromwell's face darkened anew. "Sir Harry Vane!" he exclaimed. "Good Lord, deliver me from Sir Harry Vane!" Seizing a bayonet from a nearby guard, he rushed upon the startled members and drove them pell-mell into the streets; then he locked the doors and returned to the palace.

He later tried to justify this outrage by saying it was not premeditated. But what of that? 'Tis a wonder murder and mayhem did not result from this violent display of temper and tyranny. It makes one wonder whether he is really as reluctant to rule as he claims. Harry and his wife are back at Raby Castle, where he has resumed his writing of theological and political tracts. God bless him! He like George Fox, has been a light in the darkness.

Kendal
[*Seventh month*] *Westmorland*

Over the mountains and beside the lakes. I am traveling with George Fox and a small band to Northumberland, where George wishes to confront several Puritan ministers who have been writing against him. The weather is perfect, the people cordial. We meet frequently in meadow or house with small groups who listen eagerly to George as he relates his experiences in the Lord. They feed us bountifully of their plain fare and bed us warmly with their coarse sheets and straw ticks. A far cry from Mother's fine linens and Admiral Penn's red wines! But their hearts are kind and generous, their handclasps warm and sincere, and I find that is all that really matters.

Raby Castle

We rest here a few days at the Vanes' country home. George explored the grounds and buildings like a child, and was entranced with the octagon drawing room. He and Harry had several long talks, but there is not much agreement between them.

Durham-on-Wear

This ancient fortress town, buffeted by the damp North Sea winds, is dominated by the ancient castle of the prince-bishops and by the Norman cathedral, both of whose grim and foreboding aspects loom from their chilly eminence; and the people too are grim and cold, and 'tis discouraging, nay, crushing, to me to perceive the hostility in their voices and manner as we invite their attendance at our meetings.

[*Eighth month*] *Newcastle-on-Tyne*

This is bloody Newcastle, founded on the Roman Wall by Robert, son of the Conqueror, and scene of savage attacks by the Scots, who here surrendered Charles to Parliament for execution. Our arrival here was well heralded. A number of small boys hanging over the bridge recognized George's hat and suit at once and dashed off to the town crying, "The man in leathern breeches has come!" Three or four dogs barked excitedly at our heels, and all along the street curious faces stared from hastily opened windows. Several pompous gentlemen scowled when we greeted them, and a shivering ne'er-do-well in rags pranced behind with crude and vulgar mockery. The grime and soot from many chimneys lay thick on the shops; black dust from the mines bit our skins and pricked our eyes; sharp gusts swirled our petticoats and tore at the men's hats as we approached the square, where a small delegation awaited us.

A tall, stout, blonde-haired man stepped forward and lifted a hand in warning. "Depart, ye infidels!" he commanded in ringing tones. "Go back whence ye came! Sully not our minds with your errors! Seduce not our people with your false doctrines!" I started involuntarily. Where had I heard that voice before, seen those blue eyes blazing furiously at some hapless wretch? "Depart, ye vipers, to Satan's unholy pit, before the wrath of the Lord falls upon you!" Then I knew: 'Twas Thomas Welde, he who had so shamefully betrayed and accused Anne Hutchinson! His gaze fell upon me, and slowly his eyes widened in recognition. "So, Mistress Dyer," he sneered, "you learned nothing from your experiences in Boston. Now you seek to spread your poisonous heresies here. Do you never fear that divine judgment will fall upon you as it did upon Mistress Hutchinson?"

My limbs were quivering with excitement, but I spoke up boldly. "Indeed, Sir, we must all come to divine judgment one day. 'Tis not for myself I fear, for I follow a God of love and mercy; but I do tremble for thee and thy kind, who do beat truth from thy doors and flog charity through the streets!"

My companions looked 'round, first in mild surprise, then approval, at this my first public utterance throughout the journey. Mr. Welde's rosy cheeks darkened and his round face became one great scowl. "Seize them!" he cried. "Drive them from our midst! Harry them to the ends of the earth!" He was beside himself with rage.

The other ministers and onlookers needed no second invitation. They pummeled us vigorously and tore at our cloaks, and quite frequently pounded their fellow townsmen in their ardor. Our male companions huddled about us women in protection, taking the blows meekly upon their bowed shoulders. Even so, I received one or two sharp cuffs and was more than glad to retreat hastily when several local Quakers appeared and led us to their homes.

I thank God I was given courage to speak and to sustain the blows, but my heart shudders at the thought of possible future violence. However, with these brave Friends beside me I can do naught but act as bravely and meekly as they.

[*Ninth month*] *Swarthmore Hall*

I rest here again a few days before starting the arduous journey home. I have been away from my dear children far too long—little Charlie will not remember me.

Our stay in Newcastle proved to be a fruitful one in spite of its inauspicious beginning. We did not venture to preach in the streets, but a number of the townspeople came to our private meetings, secretly at first, then openly. Some came once from curiosity and never returned; others, however, drank in the wine of our witness like thirsty travelers in the hot Sahara. At George Fox's suggestion I told of the cruel persecution in New England and of the haven Providence Plantations affords to all. George plans to send one of his friends there in due time.

He and Margaret have been writing countless letters since our return, trying to gather Friends into some kind of order. Each congregation, or meeting as it is called, will be autonomous, with one or two elders to arrange details and transact business. Heretofore there have been no regular meetings in some places, but George feels each group should meet on First day and once or twice additionally through the week. Then, too, meetings in the same district should meet every two or three weeks to maintain that close unity of both spirit and experience which is vital to the faith.

[*Eleventh month*] *Glastonbury*

Home again! How good it is to be settled for a while and to hold my little ones tightly in my arms! The jolting of the coach, the icy blasts, the strange beds and curious faces—all these are over for a time. Safe now within the loving family circle I shall renew my strength; and, examining the purposes of my life and the inclinations of my soul, I may come to some decision regarding the questions which trouble me and the factors which have unduly prolonged my stay in England.

Cromwell has been named Lord Protector of the Commonwealth and will take to himself most of the power formerly residing in the council and in Parliament.

1654-1657

[*First month, 1654*]

The coming of a new year has brought with it the realization of a new life for me, a life of total commitment to God. Whereas I have heretofore endeavored sincerely to be a good Christian, to be kind and loving, and to help those in distress, I now realize these things are not enough. It is not enough to give God whatever time is left after caring for one's family, or whatever money is left after providing for one's needs. Faith in God and love of God involve a great deal more than that. They require that we place ourselves completely in God's care and literally "take no thought of the morrow." God *will* feed us and clothe us, God *will* provide in his own way. These things have been opened to me, not alone by reflection but also by a feeling as of the Spirit working within me, so that I am convinced that I must give up my old life and begin anew.

Relinquishing the close bonds of friends and family and the comfort and privileges of wealth, and fully realizing the dangers and sorrows that may befall me, I am now prepared to shoulder faithfully whatever burdens the

Lord may require. Though I be cursed and reviled, though I be cast into the foulest dungeon, though I be flayed at the post, yea, even though I be threatened with all the tortures of the rack and brand, yet, God helping, will I never depart from the path whereunto I have set my feet.

The children shall return to Newport at the first opportunity.

Aldersgate
[*Third month*] *London*

Francis Howgill and Edward Burrough, two of George Fox's most powerful preachers, have settled at the Bull and Mouth Inn and begun the gathering of London Friends. I have taken a small house near them as I will be working closely with them, not only in preaching but in writing the countless letters which are necessary to inform others, and in answering those which sustain us. I shall also use our family's influence toward bettering prison conditions and promoting greater religious tolerance.

Already I have visited Oliver Cromwell. He received me somewhat brusquely, wearing an old gray coat not worth a shilling. I reminded him of our family connections at court and related our experiences in the New World, dwelling on the religious persecution there. He was particularly interested in my account of Anne Hutchinson's ordeal; and when I mentioned that John Wheelwright had set off the conflagration, he chuckled, "My old Cambridge friend! I can remember when I was more afraid of meeting him at football than I have been since of meeting an army in the field, for he was sure to give me a good drubbing."

We then resumed our talk on a more cordial basis, and I finally left with assurances of his good will and the promise that he would look into prison conditions and remind the judges that failure of Friends to render hat honor was not a civil offense. Alas! Many of the judges are staunch Calvinists who use their office to harass persons of other religious beliefs; or they are men opposed to Cromwell politically and thus ignore his edicts if they think they can do so with impunity.

Roger Williams is presently visiting his blind friend, John Milton, whom he instructs in the Dutch language. Indeed, since Mr. Williams' meager funds have become depleted, he has engaged to teach that language to a number of Parliament members' sons. He is without doubt a man of great intelligence and enormous erudition; but even more, he has a kind and gentle heart.

Therefore, if he decides to return to New England, I shall confidently entrust my precious children to his loving care for the long journey home.

[*Fourth month*]

Mr. Williams departed some days ago for Providence, taking with him letters from the highest officials offering encouragement to the plantations, warnings to our neighbors to desist from further interference, and appeals to all to advance liberty of conscience throughout the colonies.

A letter from Mother informs me that he remained overnight there and left next morning with the children. Through perils of the storm and dangers of the deep, God grant them safe and speedy passage. Poor things! They are too young now to comprehend the reasons for this prolonged separation, but perhaps in time they will come to understand that God's will must come before man's desires. Meanwhile life here must go on and I must fulfill the obligations I have undertaken.

London—1654

[*Fifth month*]

William Aspinwall, our old friend of Boston and early Newport days, called this month, having heard of my presence here. Suspected of sedition, he left Newport for Connecticut; but not liking the political and religious atmosphere there, this wretched man returned to Boston and apologized for his part in the Hutchinson-Wheelwright affair. His recanting evoked only well-deserved scorn, and so he came back to England some ten years ago and now makes shoes for a living. He also spends much time preaching that the millennium will come in twenty years. He explained to me how he had arrived at this date, but it seems very complicated and rather farfetched. In Ireland Archbishop Ussher has declared that God created the earth on the twenty-sixth day of Eighth month, 4004 years before Christ, at nine o'clock in the morning! He has not explained how he arrived at his figures, but the method is undoubtedly quite as complex as Mr. Aspinwall's.

In the North George Fox was busy until recently speaking and winning converts to truth—and occupying one gaol after another. Released from Carlisle prison a few months ago, and seeing that northern Friends were well established, he journeyed south to Whetstone in Leicestershire. There he was arrested by Colonel Hacker for not swearing allegiance to Cromwell. The colonel accepted George's explanations against oath-taking and said he was free to go home but had better not attend meetings or address them. To this George could not agree, for he felt it would make him appear guilty. He was then brought to London and ordered before Cromwell.

"Peace be in this house," he said upon entering, for so said the disciples before him. They talked earnestly for sometime and much about religion, George explaining that he was sent of God to witness against violence and to turn people from darkness to light.

Several times Cromwell eagerly interjected, "Yes, yes, it is truth." But at last the press of other business brought the meeting to an end. When they parted, there were tears in the great Protector's eyes.

George was allowed to go free, having worn his hat the whole time without a word of protest from the Protector!

An interesting sequel to this incident is the fact that Captain Dury, who had had charge of George and often taunted him with trembling and quaking, returned a few days later and said that as he was resting on his bed, a trembling fit suddenly came upon him so that he could not rise. He knew immediately it was the Lord's hand shaking him, and he vowed he would never again speak ill of Quakers and their trembling. A group of officers were similarly affected during a visit with George. Thus do we see how wonderfully God works through his chosen ones.

[*Ninth month*]

Will writes that things are going better in the plantations now that Roger Williams has returned. At the assembly in Seventh month Mr. Williams was elected president, and all towns were formally reunited into one government. Business is good, Will has paid off the mortgage, the children are well, and Mr. Coddington is quiet; but who can tell how long this well-deserved peace will last?

Sam has been to Boston several times to see young Anne Hutchinson. He is certainly old enough to marry, but it saddens me to realize he will soon be leaving our home for one of his own. I see no prospect of returning to Newport in the near future. Thousands flock to our meetings, and there are numerous other places where we must carry the Word. To live in Christ is everything, to live without him naught. But there remains in spite of all my work and prayers a certain loneliness which only the embraces of my dear family can dispel.

[*Twelfth month*]

George went again to see Cromwell, but the jealous priests, clustered about the Protector like flies about a cake, prevented an audience, so he has gone to Reading.

Word comes from Will that Sam and Anne were married a day or two after Sam's birthday. He says she is a sweet, modest, capable girl, and Mary agrees. Mary says further that she has charmed Sam away from privateering to dry land and milling, and, as a result, Will too has resigned his commission! A jewel she must be, as her dear grandmother was. They have built a house some distance from ours.

[*Third month, 1655*]

George Fox is back in London, adding hundreds of convincements to our already swollen number. Three thousand have come to us in the past year, and the steady stream continues. How the words pour from his mouth when he speaks—although at some meetings when we all wait expectantly he never says anything—, and how raptly we all listen! Yesterday he related to another great crowd his mission in life as it was revealed to him:

"I was sent that people might learn to do as Christ did—to visit the sick, to care for the widow and orphan, to feed the stranger at their gate. Then would there be fewer of the Lord's children ragged and maimed to beg in the snow for scraps of bread. Oh, how hardhearted are many who say they love God!

"I was called to sweep away the Jewish rites, the heathen rites, all worldly superstitions, and the schools for making priests who preach right long and loud and fatten themselves at the people's expense, but who teach not in Christ's way, simply and tenderly, and, above all, freely. Ah, when I hear the bells calling people to worship my heart cries out, for each bell is like a market bell to gather people together, that the priest may sell the Scriptures which Christ gave freely to all men!

"I was not placed on earth to be comfortable, or beautiful," he declared, scowling indignantly at a woman in satin and furs, "but to stir up others out of their comfort; not to doff my hat to, or bend my leg to, or 'you' every man who by chance of birth felt himself of greater worth than his fellowman. Are the rich without sin? Are the powerful without error? Are the proud without shame? I am called to preach to rich and poor alike; to censure the judge and the criminal if need be; to remind the innkeeper not to serve his customers too much ale lest they fall by the wayside; to encourage the schoolmaster to teach his pupils sobriety and honesty by his own example; to see that parents instruct their children and servants in the Scriptures and in Christ's way.

"Ah,"—he smiled wryly and with a pretended wince—"how many kicks and blows, pummelings and punchings have I endured for Christ. But I count them all as naught and thank God I am called to suffer in his name. Go and do ye likewise!"

George is so forthright that no one can relax or be smug when he speaks. Francis and Edward, too, are powerful speakers. But I suppose it is only natural that sometimes the smaller meetings should be unfruitful. Occasionally there is the vibrant feeling which I experienced at my first meeting, but more often there is the quiet serenity of understanding and agreement. And sometimes the meeting is downright dull and I have to pinch myself to stay awake! After all, one cannot live on a high plane of ecstasy all the time.

The continual rapid pace of life here is too much for me. I have decided to assist George by following after him and trying to bring the various meetings into some kind of order. An aged, widowed Friend will manage this house for me and use it to accommodate traveling and homeless Friends.

Quakers are now required to swear that they abjure papal authority and the doctrine of transubstantiation. Accordingly we must prepare for prison; for while we do heartily abjure these doctrines, we will not swear.

[*Fourth month*] *Cogshall*

Many convincements.

[*Fifth month*] *Yarmouth*

A few gathered here in this fishing town of extremely narrow lanes. Methinks the townsfolk's minds are equally narrow. Near here George was arrested on a trumped-up charge, but he admonished the justice to fear the Lord and was let go.

Also preaching here is a Yorkshire man, Marmaduke Stevenson. While plowing in the fields this spring, he heard the Lord's voice say to him, "I have ordained thee a prophet unto the nations." Immediately he left his plow and is now one of our most persuasive preachers.

Cambridge

Here the priestly scholars, rude and raging because of George's views, tried mightily to unseat him from his horse, but he was too skillful for them. When the inn people asked what they would have for supper, George exclaimed with a chuckle, "Had the Lord's hand not protected us, those scholars would have had us for supper!"

'Twas here in the shadow of the university library with its chained books and equally chained minds that young Mary Fisher and her middle-aged friend Elizabeth Williams were stripped to the waist and whipped at the market cross for preaching against the priests (of course, the actual charge was vagrancy); and here did they fall to their knees and pray forgiveness for their persecutors.

[*Sixth month*] *Tewkesbury*

A large meeting.

Warwick

Here George and his friends were viciously stoned as the bailiff himself looked on, not heeding Cromwell's noble proclamation of religious tolerance. Miraculously George escaped unbruised.

From Chester we hear that Richard Sale has walked through the town barefoot and in sackcloth and ashes as a sign for sinners to give up their worldly ways and clothe themselves with righteousness.

[*Eighth month*] *Bedfordshire*

Many convinced.

Baldock

Here George raised a woman thought to be dying. She and her husband were convinced and now hold great meetings at their house.

[*Ninth month*] *London*

How good it is to rest again! The work here continues at a hectic pace, with thousands being convinced. There is much writing for me to do and occasional preaching, but—thank goodness—little walking. 'Tis no wonder so many are convinced, for the example of Quakers may be even more persuasive than the preaching. Going into several shops recently to buy material for one or two new gowns, I found that Quaker shopkeepers set a fair price for their goods and stick to it with rich and poor alike; they are courteous to all, including children; they sell nothing shoddy; and they are honest, giving correct change even to the youngsters. What a contrast are other shopkeepers—haggling, rude, noisy, and thieving!

Mother will no doubt say I am extravagant to buy fine linen, but these clothes will have to last many years, as I cannot spare the time or thought in future for such mundane things, and "best's cheapest in the end." I have bought black and gray cloth, for though they are somber colors and not to my liking, they show the dirt less than other hues and so will require less care.

'Tis not only the poor and unknown who are oppressed here. Harry Vane has been imprisoned at Carisbrooke Castle on the Isle of Wight for his recent tract on civil and religious liberty, *A Healing Question*. Although Harry meant no disrespect or harm to Cromwell, his paper unfortunately struck a responsive chord among the Anabaptists, who recklessly set off on a course of violence and sedition. As the treasury remains low, Cromwell sought to augment it by seizing Harry's estates, but in this he was prevented by Parliament. Well, at least Harry is comfortable and well treated at the Castle—'tis not like being a common prisoner in a filthy gaol.

Ives—1656

Ryegate
Dorchester
[*Eleventh month*] *Weymouth*

The Channel winds blow chill and damp;
They 'most extinguish truth's bright lamp.
My body burns, my limbs do ache;
But preach I must for Christ's dear sake.

Travel is very difficult these days for Friends everywhere. We must take to the fields and bushes whenever we hear or see someone approach, for it is now unlawful for us to use the roads. What further harassments will our persecutors think of?

Will writes that the assembly has ordered two people in each town to provide a house for "public entertainment," with a large sign before it. Only those houses willing to provide both food and beds for travelers are allowed to serve liquors, and a good thing, too, for travel is terribly difficult in New England. Also, this requirement will tend to keep down the number of drunken men lurching about the streets and getting into everyone's way. Mercy! It is simply dreadful in the cities here at night. I hate to think of our children's being exposed to such disgusting sights, but of course they ought to be in bed soon after dark. I hope Will isn't too lenient with them; he has such a soft heart for them—and such a soft head for some other matters!

Totness
Plymouth
[*Third month, 1656*] *Ives*

Young Mary Fisher and Ann Austin, a middle-aged Friend and mother like me, have sailed for Barbados to bring our message to the New World.

[*Fourth month*] *Launceston*

I have seen Friends in prison here in the castle keep atop a steep hill, and I fear the terrible stench of the place will linger in my hair and clothes forever despite my vigorous washing. At least I have rid myself of the lice which quickly invaded my garments in the short time I was there.

After being confined for a number of weeks, our friends were brought before the judge. They angered him by declining to doff hats, argued with him about the biblical mention of hats, and confounded him with their knowledge of the Bible. In a rage he tore their Bibles from them; then lies were sworn against them by the witnesses.

The wicked gaoler put them into a nasty, noisome hole they call Doomsdale, where he refused them bed or straw—so that they had to stand up all night or lie in the twenty-years' accumulation of filth—and sufficient food. However, after several weeks the local magistrate heard of these abominable conditions and ordered the gaoler to remedy them. George and his companions were only too glad to do his work for him and cleaned the place as well as men can, but the odor and insects remain.

Humphrey Norton, one of our London Friends, wrote to Oliver Cromwell offering to take George's place here, but was denied. However, Cromwell is reported to have said, "What man would do as much for me? Would that I could inspire such devotion in my followers!" Would that he might indeed languish for a term in Doomsdale and see for himself how vile the gaols are and how little the laws are heeded! I fear for George and his companions, as the gaoler is a surly, cruel beast; but as there is nothing I can do, and as there are a few Friends here now who will look after them, I shall go on with the preaching.

One of the youngest, yet also one of the most powerful

of our preachers, Little James Parnell, has died of injuries resulting from his gaoler's cruelty. Slight of stature he was great of heart; frail of body he was strong of spirit; a mere boy he yet possessed a brilliant intellect. The memory of his unflinching courage, his Christ-like meekness, his tremendous, living faith will remain in our hearts for years to come. Now may his broken body rest in peace and his soul with God.

Okehampton, Exeter
Tiverton, Taunton

Tors, churches, cathedrals, walls, castles, markets.

[*Sixth month*] *Glastonbury*

Once again I rest at home, a quieter, sadder home without my little ones, but Mother's warm and patient love renews my frail body, and letters from Will and the children gladden my heart. Please God I may return to them soon.

George is still in Launceston gaol. However, the Protector, hearing of his imprisonment, ordered an investigation. The gaoler has been told to mind his manners and to let the prisoners have more food; they are also allowed to walk about outside occasionally. For although the magistrates mistreat us cruelly for refusing to swear, they do believe us when we give our word and know the men will not attempt to escape.

Hugh Peter (in the vanguard of those hounding Anne Hutchinson), at present one of the Protector's priests, warned Cromwell that imprisonment was the best means of advancing George's cause. Cromwell replied that that might be, he would just have to take that chance. For while he has a great interest in George and respects him, he cannot interfere when any Friend breaks the civil law.

We do not mind that—we are prepared to suffer for our law-breaking. What causes us the most suffering is that so many people in power themselves break the law or ignore it to persecute us!

[*Eighth month*]

George has been released, so I must begin the weary trudging again.

Bristol

Christopher Holder, a young, wealthy, and well-educated man living near here, has recently been convinced and is proving to be a powerful preacher. He tells me that in some places all the adult Quakers are in prison, yet the children faithfully continue meeting.

London

While riding near Hyde Park, George came upon the Protector in his coach and rode some distance beside him, haranguing him steadily about the vile persecutions and hard sufferings of Friends. Invited to Cromwell's house, George exhorted him to acknowledge the light of Christ which enlightens every man, but to no avail.

Yorkshire abbeys
Holderness, Humber
[*Eleventh month*] *Leicestershire grasslands*

Staffordshire moors
[*Twelfth month*] *Worcestershire*

All towns look alike now to my weary eyes, all streets are equally rough to my aching feet. Surely George, iron man though he is, must now begin to curtail his many labors. We do not all have his seven-league boots and Samsonian strength!

Warwickshire, Gloucestershire, Oxford

Beautiful spires and gardens, old buildings, cold hearts.

[*Second month, 1657*] *London*

Margaret Fell writes that two women Friends have run naked through nearby Ulverston streets and asks what she shall advise other Friends about it. George has replied that of course the women did not do this of their own accord, therefore no blame can be attached to them. Their action was the result of a call, an inward urge from God, to show that the people there are not clothed with truth. George sent them warm greetings and tender sympathy for the cruel flogging they endured; at the same time he urged others to be sure the call is genuine before they take similar action.

My own mind and heart have been sorely troubled by this incident, and I have wondered over and over what reasons could have moved decent men to such a bestial act. These were modest, humble, devout women. Yet because they heard the voice of God so loud in their ears and felt his love so strong in their hearts that they could not deny his will, they have been savagely beaten until their backs were bloody and raw.

Is this also to be my lot? Separation from loved ones I can endure; pain I can bear; death I might stoically embrace. But to stand, clothed only in righteousness, before a hostile, jeering mob—I shudder at the prospect and pray fervently that this cup may pass from me.

Kent—1657

[*Third month*]

The hop gardens of Kent. The Pilgrims' Way through wooded Surrey. Walk, stumble, crawl—over muddy roads, through brambly fields, up hill, down dale. Preach and pray—in streets, homes, steeple houses, forest glades.

Berkshire
Gloucestershire
Wales

No rest for the weary. Jeers, amens, crickets chirping, birds trilling, cows lowing. The soft sweet misty greens of spring.

Glastonbury

O blessed relief! O saving surcease from the swollen feet, the aching limbs, the rasping throat! The sweetness of spring engulfs me and I give myself up to renewal and re-creation. My muddy garments scrubbed, my graying locks now clean and brushed, I sit and talk and read.

Margaret writes that her husband no longer attends his own church but sits quietly by himself in an adjoining room with the door open when Friends meet at the Hall for worship. His understanding and forbearance have encouraged large numbers in the area to join Friends, and his influence has protected them from some harassment.

Margaret also chides me in her letters for my dull wardrobe and remarks that many Friends are giving up gay colors for the drab. "There's no sin in color, nor in wearing it," she says, "if the material be not an extravagance. But after all, black is more practical for those of us who plod through mud and dust and dodge the garbage of the mob!

No word has reached us concerning the whereabouts or condition of Ann Austin and Mary Fisher or, indeed, of my own family.

While I have been resting here, it has been clearly opened to me that my work in England is done and that I must return home. I ought not to leave the proselytizing of my chosen land to those who know it not. Having published truth abroad, I now must publish it at home; for all men, indifferent, wicked, or depraved though they be, are yet entitled to be told the truth, that they may receive and profess it. I have therefore resolved to set out shortly for the long and arduous journey home.

Plymouth

Tenderly once more have I embraced my dearest Mother, whose love and understanding have sustained me through the trials of many years. Fondly have I gazed again upon the scenes of childhood, sweet scenes which I shall see no more. And sad at heart, though strong in purpose, I now depart for aye these well-loved shores.

Here did I achieve maturity—of heart, and soul, and mind; and list'ning, heard the voice of truth: that God is love, peace, justice, mercy, kindness—and forgiveness. For if I deal kindly, justly, and peaceably with my fellowmen but forgive them not for their transgressions against me, do I not smother the divine inward light with the pall of hate?

So, as I leave these beloved scenes and faces and return perhaps to those which once seemed evil, I do wholeheartedly renounce and leave behind all feelings of bitterness and ill will—toward jeering mobs, toward pompous priests, toward all those men and women who neither see the light as I see it nor understand the Word as I understand it. Through God's grace has my soul been cleansed; and through that grace may I receive the strength, wisdom, and courage to do his will.

1657-1658

[*Fourth month, 1657*] *Boston* gaol

Alas! How wretched is my situation—my work halted before it is begun, my life and that of my friend threatened by the unjust and obstinate rulers of this city. Our Bibles have been taken from us and given to the surly gaoler, we lack any sort of bed or cover, the food is scanty and poor, and the windows have been boarded up so that no one may speak to us; for even sympathizers are punished here. If only Will's letters had not gone astray, I should have known of this infamous law which bans all Quakers from the colony for fomenting sedition and rebellion through our religious principles. Ignorance of the law is no excuse, the authorities say, so Anne Burden and I must be punished. Innocent though we are of any crime—except that of advocating and practicing freedom of conscience—still we must suffer whatever penalties these fear-filled and misguided people have devised.

Next day

Will has come. He must sign a large bond and take me straight back to Rhode Island without stopping along the way or permitting me to speak with anyone, lest I poison and subvert some weak mind.

Anne Burden, poor soul, who only came to settle her late husband's estate here, will be sent penniless back to England on the same ship which brought us; and the captain of the ship, also ignorant of the law, must pay a fine of £100 for bringing us here!

[*Fifth month*] *Newport*

At last we are safely home in a tolerant, free community. How good it is to hold my children tightly in my arms! How I marvel at their great size and sweet faces! Young Willie is a tall, strong lad, and little Charlie a darling, mischievous imp; gentle, capable Mary is betrothed; and Maher, Anne, and Harry are sturdy, willing helpers in field and house. But the grandest sight of all is that of Sam's firstborn lying in my lap. "My cup runneth over. Surely goodness and mercy shall follow me all the days of my life."

A long talk with Will has given me a clear picture of the momentous events taking place in the colonies during the past year. "Will," I began, "was there any news of Mary Fisher and Ann Austin? The last I heard, they were traveling to Barbados and hoped to come on to Rhode Island from there."

"Indeed there was news of them, my dear. They reached Barbados safely late in 1655 and gathered a number of believers together. They then set sail in the *Swallow* for Boston, preaching every day to the sailors, and arriving in Fifth month of last year. Upon landing, one or two disgruntled crewmen reported to the authorities that two dangerous heretics were aboard, and if they were let loose upon the town, it would be Anne Hutchinson all over again! Furthermore, both Thomas Welde and Christopher Marshall, ministers in England . . ."

"Of whom I had some experience," I murmured.

". . . had written violent letters to Boston describing Quakers as advocating *'horrid opinions, diabolical doctrines, mutiny, sedition, rebellion, and the overthrow of the established church and commonwealth. . . .'* Since Governor Endecott was absent, Mr. Bellingham took charge. He ordered the two to remain on board while he searched the ship for heretical books, of which he claimed to have found one hundred. These he ordered the hangman to burn at the marketplace. Then the women were stripped and searched for witch signs on their bodies—luckily none were found—and hustled to gaol."

"On what charge?" I demanded.

"On a charge of being Quakers."

"But Will . . ."

"Of course, my dear, there is no law against being a Quaker, but that was the charge anyway. Mr. Bellingham was extremely agitated at this time as his sister-in-law had recently been hanged on a charge of witchcraft, and I suppose he felt he must act so zealously that no possible suspicion could involve *him* in a similar unpleasant experience.

"Old Nicholas Upsal, impressed by the women's stout faith and the injustice of the matter, ventured to comfort them through the windows until these were boarded up, and after that paid the gaoler from his own purse to supply them with adequate, nourishing food. Still, their cell was totally dark and of course damp; fortunately the weather at that time was warm.

"After a while the General Court got around to hearing the case and decided that the ladies were not heretics. . . ."

"How exceedingly broad-minded of them!" I exclaimed.

He chuckled and went on. "But the verdict was that their books and beliefs might prove harmful to the colony. And so their Bibles and bedding were given to the gaoler for his fee; but Captain Kempthorn was forced to return them without pay to Barbados with a warning not to transport any more such undesirables; and the townsfolk were warned not to speak with any Quakers upon pain of £5 fine. Upon his return, Governor Endecott frowned at Bellingham and declared that *he* would have whipped the women soundly!

"Two days later the *Speedwell* arrived from London with not two but eight Quakers on board! Obviously this influx called for stronger action.

"Marched into court by Governor Endecott, the old army officer who had himself once been brought before the court on religious charges, the Quakers were questioned minutely by the ministers about their religious beliefs. So few conflicts were brought out that one magistrate at last turned to Mr. Norton and demanded impatiently, 'Just what are the differences between you and the Quakers?' But he was quickly hushed.

"The governor, displeased that Friends could be convicted only of civil offenses, cut short the proceedings with an ominous warning: 'Take care that you do not break our ecclesiastical laws, for then you are sure to stretch by a halter.'

"The court then passed a law aimed directly at protecting the colony from religious toleration and freedom, and other Quaker views. This law provides for immediate banishment of Quakers, burning of their books, and fines for anyone upholding their opinions or criticizing the magistrates or ministers. The church then decreed a day of public humiliation in all the New England Puritan churches as penance for the contamination by thy friends.

"After several weeks in gaol, where they were frequently badgered by Norton and Endecott, these Friends also were returned to London. Sam Gorton had offered them asylum in his colony, but they were not allowed to go there."

" 'Tis amazing some word did not reach me concerning all this," I murmured, "but I was traveling so much of the time . . ."

"Aye," said Will, "and I know that at least one ship carrying letters from us went down, and 'tis likely others may have been captured by the Dutch.

"But to continue: The authorities were determined to stamp out this little grass fire before it could gain any headway. So, when the crier and drummer read the new law through the streets and Mr. Upsal stood in his doorway shouting his disagreement in his usual vigorous and forthright language, they haled him before the court. They charged him for being absent from church—as he was, from sympathy with the Quakers—and for speaking against the authorities. He warned them earnestly to turn from this severe and narrow-minded course, but they only snarled and banished him from the colony. If the Indians had not befriended him and conducted him to friends in Sandwich, he would have perished in the snow.

"However, thou and Mistress Burden were lucky indeed. I fear harsher penalties are in store for future dissenters."

I had to agree. Remembering the great numbers of Friends in England and their inexhaustible zeal in spreading the message, I knew that soon other shiploads of Quakers would arrive to storm the gates of Boston.

And what was I to do? Could I sit comfortably at home while foreign Friends braved the dangers of my own land?

Could I restrict my preaching to the tolerance and safety of Rhode Island? Or had I been called home for greater service; had Will's letters gone astray as part of God's plan for me? Have I been clearly shown the way upon which I am to set my feet? I must have time to think and pray, but the sands of time are running out.

Events are moving rapidly. Today a tiny boat—I can hardly call it a ship—named the *Woodhouse* anchored in the harbor. Aboard were the original *Speedwell* party, except for five who disembarked at New Amsterdam, and several newcomers to our shores—Mary Clarke, Robert Hodgson, Humphrey Norton, whom I knew in London, Richard Doudney, and the merchant-preacher, William Robinson. 'Tis a miracle they arrived at all as the boat is hardly seaworthy and the captain knew no navigation and possessed no compass; but the Great Navigator steered them personally through storm and darkness to our shores.

We welcomed them all heartily and gathered in our house for thankful worship and a discussion of how best the party could proceed with its mission. Christopher Holder and John Copeland will make their way northward along the island and coastal colonies as far as Salem, while Mary Clarke insists on going alone to Boston. We urged them to be cautious and to avoid inflaming the Bay authorities, but they are like most young folk—impatient of their elders. They have set their feet toward the goal of freedom of conscience, they declare, and neither our warnings nor Boston's punitive measures will turn them from their chosen path. They leave in a few days.

Our intrepid Friends have departed, confident they will meet with some success. My prayers are with them constantly; and Catharine Scott's daughter Mary, who is visiting us, also seems to be praying somewhat harder than usual. She was noticeably impressed with Christopher's charming manners and handsome appearance.

[*Seventh month*]

On Long Island Robert Hodgson and twenty or thirty other Friends have aroused the fierce opposition of Governor Stuyvesant. Their protests and pleas for religious liberty have so far been unavailing.

Here in Providence Plantations has been circulated a letter from the United Colonies declaring that numerous Quakers in the colonies are a disruptive and divisive influence—not to say, nuisance—with their strange doctrines and sometimes peculiar behavior. It goes on to insist that the plantations have become a refuge (which they have, thank God!) and a breeding place (may it be so!) for the sect, and demands that Friends be expelled at once for the good of all the colonies. No reply has yet been made.

In Plymouth Governor Bradford has died. He was a genuinely good man, just toward the Indians, simple and honest in his life and, bless his heart! a preacher of short sermons.

[*Eighth month*]

Several Friends have settled in this colony and are making their presence felt—spiritually, financially, politically. Will came home to report on an assembly meeting one day and remarked that he had mentioned to a Friend the bitter feelings evoked by a certain vote. The Friend nodded, then said, "Would it not have been better, Friend Dyer, to have postponed action until there was more general agreement?"

"Why, man, you can't do business that way!" exclaimed Will. "You have to vote to get things done."

"Nay, Friend," the other replied. "If ill will results, 'tis better to delay the matter. Few affairs are so urgent that they require immediate action, particularly at the sacrifice of harmony. Moreover, in our meetings for business we do not vote at all. All who wish to speak on the matter at hand do so, and when everyone has finished, we take the general sense or comment as the basis for any action. If there is no clear sense we postpone the matter. This way we consider everyone's views, avoid hasty action, and, most important, foster feelings of individual worth, cooperation, and good will rather than of opposition and bitterness."

Will was still dubious about it when he returned home, but I have assured him that I know its effectiveness.

Willie, Maher, Anne, and Harry have joined Mary and me in attending Friends' meetings. Sam, of course, remains closer to his father; and little independent Charlie, the second apple of his father's eye, trots along beside his idol. I feared Will might be unhappy and difficult over these changes, but he has only indicated some uneasiness about the children's safety. I have assured him I will not involve the younger ones in anything dangerous; the older ones must make their own decisions.

Will has altered considerably during the years of our separation. The old fire and temper have subsided; arguments on scientific theories and religious differences are no longer raised; any once controversial activities on my part are no longer questioned. He seems quite content for us just to be together again and makes every effort for our declining years to pass in harmony, in spite of the continued differences between us. We differ but are not divided. Dear man! Now that Mr. Coddington too has become a Friend, even that thorn has been removed, and they speak pleasantly to each other when they meet.

Nicholas Upsal's two sons have joined him here, and all three are now Friends. Others include John Clarke's son Walter, Nicholas Easton, William Brenton, and John Coggeshall's son Joshua.

Oh, what terrible news we hear! Poor Mary Clarke, fainting from exhaustion, staggered a few days ago into Providence on the arm of a friendly Indian. Flogged, then imprisoned for twelve weeks in Boston, she was at last released, escorted some distance toward the Massachusetts border, and savagely thrust into the wild forest without food, wraps, or protection of any kind. Now Catharine Scott is nursing her back to health. Friends have called a general meeting for next week in Providence to hear the story from Mary herself.

[*Ninth month*] *Providence*

Haggard and exhausted, Mary began in a low voice to tell us of her painful ordeal:

"We set out soberly in our boat, knowing full well that we advanced toward certain suffering. Yet we knew also that there could be no turning back; for though the prospect loomed ominously before us, our belief in God's desire—that all men know his love—required us to go on.

"A few miles around the point I was set ashore. I had walked only a short distance in the woods when an Indian suddenly stepped in front of me. Greeting him in a friendly manner, I offered to share my noonday bread and cheese with him. He hesitated some moments; but seeing me unarmed and forthright in all my words and movements, he soon joined me in quiet companionship. Afterwards he offered to conduct me toward Boston.

"When I told him of my mission, however, he shook his head violently, exclaiming, 'No! No! Do not go. People with hard hearts live in that place. Their God is not thy God.' But I was not to be dissuaded, and when we reached the edge of the forest, he sadly bade me farewell.

"I trudged across the dry and dusty meadows under the blazing sun. The bees droned drowsily and only an occasional sparrow cheeped weakly from the scanty shade. Entering Roxbury, I advanced along the empty streets to the square. Here I paused to rest. A small group of women listlessly drawing water eyed me suspiciously and made no offer to relieve my thirst. Undaunted, I cleared my parched throat and addressed them cordially.

" 'My dear friends,' I said, 'I come to you from far across the sea with a message of the utmost importance. God has sent me these many miles to reveal to all men his kind and loving nature, and to proclaim that the letter of the law killeth, but the spirit giveth life. If ye toil not on the sabbath, take not the Lord's name in vain, tithe to him his rightful share; yet cheat the widow and beat the orphan, revenge yourselves upon your enemies, and deny food and drink to the stranger at your gates . . .' here my voice cracked, 'ye do deny the Lord, for he hath said, "As ye would that men should do to you, do ye also to them likewise." '

"As they began to whisper among themselves in a hostile manner, I forgot about my thirst and attempted to placate them enough to hear the rest of my message. ' "Love ye your enemies, and do good, be ye merciful, as your Father also is merciful." '

" 'Be silent!' cried one of the women sharply. 'Who invited thee to our town? We allow no vagrants to pause here and waste our substance. And who art thou to tell us what the Scriptures mean? We can read for ourselves, some of us, and if we do not understand, we pay well for a Cambridge man to interpret for us. Surely he knows more about the Bible than any ignorant woman!'

" 'Aye,' the others murmured sullenly.

"I tried to reason with them, but the angry voices grew louder and the women began to shout, 'She is one of those new heretics, those vile Quakers, come to infect our souls and destroy our ways. Call the guard!'

"So I desisted. Amid jeers and blows I was mounted on horseback and led over the flats to Boston, then shoved into a small cell. The iron-barred windows had been boarded over, and the door was solid oak bound in iron; the heat and darkness were oppressive, and I was hard put not to give way to despair; but I recalled the patient meekness and constant faith of our English Friends in similar or worse situations and soon composed myself for prayer. Shortly afterward I was sentenced to receive twenty lashes and be imprisoned for twelve weeks.

"The next day amid a vast crowd and led by drummers, I was marched to the common a mile away and ordered to strip to the waist. This I refused to do, as any woman would. The executioner then forcibly removed my clothing, bound me to the whipping post, and proceeded to carry out the sentence with a three-cord whip and a heavy hand. His own enthusiasm was increased by that of the governor, who cried, 'Lay on! Lay on! With every stroke the Devil bleeds, and with every drop of blood his damned heresies drain from her foul body!'

"The first blows bit fiercely into my flesh. I feared that I must flinch or scream; but suddenly a great feeling of peace and love flooded my entire body. Realizing that these men also possessed that of God which is in every man—although they gave it no heed—I fell to praying fervently for them, and the remaining blows were as naught.

"When it was over, Mr. Wilson raised his arms to pray: 'O God,' he droned sanctimoniously, 'deliver us from this pestilence. Drive this plague from our midst. Cleanse this woman's mind of its filthy errors, and put down her sinful nature. . . ,' and so on for what seemed an eternity, while I prayed that his own wretched mind might be cleansed and enlightened. As I walked back to my cell, I saw shock and sympathy openly expressed on many faces, and I was heartened still more.

"My trials were small compared to those of our other dear friends. I languished in the hot, dark cell without bedding or sufficient food and water—for the gaoler was a surly man and I had little money to pay him—for several weeks, frequently interrogated by the priests. Once they burst in to tell me almost gleefully that the court had passed a tongue-boring law which was sure to curb our zeal.

"You can imagine my dismay, then, when suddenly one day Christopher, John, and a Salem man, Samuel Shattuck, were thrust into the adjoining cell. However, the men said they had heard of this harsh law and were not frightened by it. And so we rejoiced greatly at our reunion and eagerly related to one another all our adventures and trials."

She paused to sip some ale and to shift to a more comfortable position, for it was obvious that her lacerated back still pained her.

"Christopher and John had much to tell: Making their way easily to Martha's Vineyard, they rose after the minister's sermon to speak fervently on one of their reasons for leaving England, namely, their refusal to pay tithes to support priests and churches in which they had no faith or interest. Incensed, some of the congregation seized and ejected them. In the afternoon they again tried to speak but were shouted down. Irate citizens, jealous of their prejudices and forgetful of the law, complained to the governor, who ordered them from the colony.

"At Sandwich many of the people welcomed them eagerly into their log houses to preach, for they were dissatisfied with the intolerance prevailing there; and in the few days Christopher and John were there, eighteen families became Friends! Other disgruntled folk, however, notified the governor, and a constable was sent to arrest them. At word of his coming the meeting quickly adjourned from the village to a small hollow in the hills, where the faithful sat on flat stones beside a quiet stream. This natural setting among the leafy trees, with the billowing clouds drifting through a blue sky, seemed to enhance the mood of worship and deepen it profoundly; so that when our friends departed, they were heartened by the knowledge that those convinced here would stand firm in the face of harsh fines or severe lashings.

"They encountered various trials along the coast and at Duxbury, where they ran afoul of Assistant Governor John Alden, who was not at all averse to applying the law but, fortunately for our friends, was prevented from harming them. They then turned inland to Mansfield and Dedham, where they were joined by Richard Doudney. They continued through Charlestown, Cambridge, and Lynn, preaching as they went and winning some Friends; and came at last to Salem, where they were well received by a number of believers. Cassandra and Lawrence Southwick graciously and bravely sheltered them.

"Here it was that Christopher again rose after service to speak; but being recognized as a Quaker, he was seized from behind and a glove thrust into his mouth to choke him. Like other Friends, he offered no resistance as his captor wrestled him toward the door with kicks and blows.

"But Samuel Shattuck was not a Friend and under no such compulsion to refrain from violence. In spite of his advanced age and the dire punishment sure to follow, he sprang to Christopher's aid, flung the stifling glove into the air, and ripped away the sleeve of the attacker, causing him to loose his victim. Thus did he save our friend's life and join his own to our great cause.

"The four men were hurried off to Boston and questioned repeatedly. Although no proof of a crime could be found, they were nevertheless sentenced to flogging and banishment. Samuel, because of his age, was only forced to promise not to attend any more Friends' meetings in the colony and then was fined £20, a great sum for him to pay. He remained several days to bandage the flayed and bleeding flesh, declaring solemnly that he could not live longer in this cruel and intolerant colony and that he would seek help for us elsewhere. During this time the men had neither food nor drink.

"When the elderly Southwicks were roughly shoved into our midst one day for having sheltered our friends, Sam decided that further delay increased the danger for other Friends; and so he parted sadly from us. He took with him, however, a letter, painfully written by Christopher after his flogging, to be circulated in Boston as a means of informing the truly righteous and just people there of the shocking practices their leaders employed in God's name.

"Although this paper aroused many sympathizers to outspoken indignation, it also aroused Governor Endecott to greater vindictiveness. 'You vile, degenerate Quakers ought to be hanged for publishing this! Verily, you are possessed by the Devil!' he railed, and forthwith decreed that Christopher be whipped twice each week for the remaining seven weeks of his gaol term: fifteen lashes the first time, three additional ones each succeeding time!

"The awful brutality of this sentence overwhelmed me, and. . . ."

Her voice failed at the memory of this cruel decree. While she sipped more ale and recovered her composure, we murmured together in shocked sympathy. But young Mary Scott fainted dead away and was carried off to her bed chamber; her heart has indeed been given to Christopher Holder. After a while, Mary Clarke resumed her account.

"About this time we heard from our surly gaoler that Boston had taken up the matter of the Quaker menace with the United Colonies and urged the secretary to request Governor Arnold to exclude them from Rhode Island, our one haven. You are familiar with this document, are you not?"

"Indeed we are," said Catharine indignantly. "Governor Arnold, however, has replied that Quakers will not be punished or driven out, for, as he said, there is no law preventing us from following our own way to salvation. 'Furthermore,' he added with great perception, 'Quakers delight in being persecuted, as they gain many more converts that way than by any of their doctrines.' "

Mary smiled slightly and went on:

"Then Christopher, John, and Richard, anxious that all should know the truth about our faith and not hear only the lies of the priests, wrote a declaration of faith, of which two copies were made. Cassandra hid one within her dress; I did likewise with the other and carried it out of gaol when I left a few days later. This paper declares our belief in God the Father, Son, and Holy Spirit as revealed in Scripture, thus refuting those who call us blasphemers and heretics.

"And so I made my way, without food, wraps, or shelter,

along the road toward Providence, until another friendly Indian assisted me to this place. By God's grace do I stand here today, and by his grace shall I continue to preach his gospel and further his work."

After pressing about her to clasp her hand and offer words of praise and encouragement, we composed ourselves to discuss what action we might take to help her and to bring light to the darkness now enshrouding our neighbors to the North. The sense of the meeting was that all who could leave their families for a time would go forth at once to wherever they felt called, and preach; and that those who were concerned for the suffering and oppression of Friends in Boston and for the general misunderstandings prevailing there would be given all material and spiritual assistance in accomplishing their mission to the lion's den.

[*Tenth month*] *Newport*

Word reaches us that Richard, John, and Christopher have made their way to Providence where Catharine and her daughters are nursing them. Christopher's health is broken from his numerous beatings. Surely he will return to England. Mary Clarke has joined Mary Weatherhead on Long Island, whence they will depart soon to winter in the warm Barbados and restore the former's health. The declaration of faith was found on Cassandra and she remains in prison after being beaten, although Lawrence has been released and strives to pay her fine.

As for myself, I feel a strong urge to travel again and preach—I who only six months ago thought I had come home to stay. But where am I to go? My mind is not yet clear on that point, so I must wait. I have told the family my decision and they have accepted it with a good spirit. Mary and Tom have announced their desire to wed, and if Friends' examining committee finds no hindrance, they will be married next month. They are to live in this house where Mary can care for the children and Will.

Dear Will! Would that we could enjoy our remaining years together, for age has touched him with blighting hands: his once fair locks are now snow-white, his hearty voice subdued; and the jaunty step is sadly slowed by aching joints. Yet we both believe no separation, hurt, or peril can now divide us or destroy our steadfast love. Our faith in God is strong, our will to do his will firm. So shall we part but ever closer be.

[*Twelfth month*] *Connecticut*

Mary and Tom were married a few days ago at home with all their friends about them. We sat for a time in silence, and as I watched Mary sitting solemnly in her blue gown beside Tom, I recalled my own marriage day. I wore a brilliant red velvet gown, with a wreath of orange blossoms and rosemary in my hair. We said our vows in the Glastonbury cathedral, then drove gaily home to sign the certificate amidst much laughter and kissing. A prodigious lunch followed, and then Will and I stole off to a cottage beyond the tor. Well, our times and beliefs are different now, and our customs must change with them. But the tears and fears of a mother for her daughter remain the same.

After a while Mary and Tom rose and pledged their lives to one another. Then Will Coddington prayed for God's blessings upon them, we clasped hands all 'round, signed the marriage certificate, and proceeded to devour the abundant repast which the girls and I had prepared—

ham, fowl, roasts, vegetables, cakes, pies, breads—everything we could provide.

When all the guests had departed, I gathered up the remaining food into several baskets along with my small traveling bag, and the entire family walked with me through the streets, leaving our food baskets with the poor.

At the edge of town I bade them all a fond farewell; and if a tear or two fell quietly, 'twas not through any fear of mine of what might be, 'twas only that my human heart could not restrain its grief at parting from these other warm and loving, gentle, tender hearts.

At last I turned away and plodded through the snow.

[*First month, 1658*] *New Haven*

Making my way through the light snow to Brenton's Point, I was conveyed to the mainland by old Mr. Brenton himself and solemnly given his heartfelt blessings as I stepped ashore. The weather, though cold, was still, and I traveled to this town in easy stages, spending the nights in isolated homes or small villages along the coast. At each place I explained my mission and described the trials of our Friends in Boston. There was much sympathy for them, although not much inclination to leave their own congregations for ours, or to take any action against the persecutors.

In New Haven, on the other hand, there is open hostility to my preaching; but Governor John Winthrop, Jr., in consideration of Will's high standing in Newport, no doubt, has so far allowed me a measure of freedom here and in the nearby villages. He is a military man, outspoken, active in public affairs; while his younger brother, Samuel, who frequently attends our meetings, is quiet and thoughtful.

How different they are from each other, and how very different both are from what the father was!

[*Second month*]

John Rous and John Copeland have arrived, bearing terrible news. "Encouraged by the good treatment received in Scituate," John Copeland began, "where the generous and tolerant magistrates not only refused to prosecute but even allowed meetings to be held at their own houses, old William Brend and I set out for Boston, confident that our safe-conduct passes would protect us from any civil harm. But we were soon disabused of that ingenuous notion by magistrate Simon Bradstreet, a notorious Quaker baiter. He clapped us into gaol along with John Rous, Humphrey Norton, William Leddra, and Thomas Harris, and viciously carried out the prescribed flogging, not sparing even William Brend. He, poor brave soul, lay neck-to-heels in irons for sixteen hours; the next day he was beaten so severely with a tarred rope that his life was despaired of —by his friends, not the authorities—and a doctor sent for, while his gaoler went dutifully off to church. A number of horrified townspeople hurriedly collected the sum needed to release all of us, but William was too ill to be moved. He was thus left to the ministrations of one or two compassionate friends. They openly and rather belligerently defied the authorities, who were astonished and somewhat chastened by this sudden uproar against the accepted order.

"Mr. Norton, in attempting to justify such harsh treatment, declared, 'William Brend has tried to wring the life from our Scriptures, and if we have beaten him black and blue, 'tis no more than he deserves!'

"At this time Sarah Gibbons and Dorothy Waugh were

also in gaol, having survived a fierce blizzard in their long walk First month from Newport to Salem. They preached there two weeks, then came to Boston, and were arrested and beaten. Even now Friends have probably paid their fines and taken them to the shelter of Rhode Island."

My heart swelled indignantly at the recital of these cruel outrages and I knew at once that I must witness more strongly against the savagery of the sanctimonious. I too must go to Boston.

[*Third month*] *Newport*

Despite my firm resolve to enter the lion's den, I was prevented by unfortunate circumstances, for I contracted a severe chill while preaching out in the cold and wet. It quickly affected my lungs and left me pitifully weak and racked with an exhausting cough. Governor Winthrop took advantage of this infirmity to order me from the colony—to prevent my becoming a public charge, he said. He then joined with the rest of Connecticut, Massachusetts, and Plymouth in a pact to fight the Quakers with every weapon, including protests to the Protector; but his brother ignored the general hostility and conducted me safely home.

All is well here: Mary and Tom are blissful, the others healthy and contented. They all assist me eagerly, for I am not yet recovered, in writing numerous letters of our trials and successes to Friends in this country and in England. Will, recently elected attorney-general and as pleased about it as a child about a sweet cake (bless his heart), has despatched a message to John Clarke in London urgently requesting him to remind the protector of our charter, and to plead that our government not be forced to exercise any civil restraint over anyone's conscience so long as

Friends break no civil ordinances. This they are not likely to do here where they are met with tolerance and forbearance, although hardly with open arms.

John Copeland rests with us a while after another ordeal. He and Christopher were flogged again last month. Afterwards they made their way to Catharine Scott's home, where Mary's charms and tender nursing proved too much for Christopher's otherwise strong character, and in spite of the dark prospect ahead they are now betrothed. As soon as he was able, John rode over here; for, he says laughingly, our bracing air has more recuperative powers than any amount of feminine attention! At any rate, he progresses well and the children adore him.

The sad tidings of the deaths of Mary Clarke and Mary Weatherhead reached us recently. They died in a shipwreck off Long Island last winter as they set sail for Barbados. Their courage was great, their faith steadfast, their purpose firm. Now God has gathered them from all mortal ills into his loving arms.

[*Fourth month*]

Humphrey Norton, William Leddra, and Thomas Harris are the latest victims of the Boston atrocities. They suffered cruelly under a new law which provides that imprisoned Quakers who refuse to work are to be whipped twice every week, the number of strokes increasing each time. Besides this, Humphrey was branded on the hand with the heretic's *H*. Our God-fearing and humane friends there again paid the men's fines, and they are recovering in Providence.

In accordance with our plan to keep some Friends in Boston at all times, however, Christopher and John were already on their way when news reached us of the others.

Newport—1658

What determination these men have! Even old William Brend has returned to Boston, and his scarcely healed back has been laid open again.

[*Fifth month*]

Christopher and John are in the lion's den awaiting the court's decision as to their fate. Brave John Rous declared, when arrested a day or two later, "I was much tempted to say I came to the town to take shipping to go to Barbados, but I could not deny him who moved me to come hither, nor his service, to avoid suffering." So he too is there in gaol. Messengers quickly inform us of each new development, and we are ready for a strong protest.

The court's sentence has been passed: Each man is to lose his right ear! How long can this evil continue; how far will these madmen go? Feeling runs high in Boston, for even some staunch Puritans decry such cruelty.

Catharine Scott, Sam Shattuck, and the Southwicks will lead a march from Rhode Island to Boston; and others from Sandwich will join them. Both will attempt to dissuade Governor Endecott from this rash policy of persecution, but their success is doubtful.

This purest of the Puritans so diligently pursues the responsibilities of his office that he permits no particle of mercy, tolerance, or reason to becloud his sense of duty. Our messenger reports that when John and Christopher were brought before him, he cried passionately, "Your ears shall be cut off!" Then, recognizing them as former offenders, his wrath was fully aroused and he roared, "What! You have not altered your heretical views since you were here last?"

"We preach the truth as the Lord has shown it us," Christopher replied steadily.

"But why have you come? Surely the law was made clear to you?"

"The Lord has commanded us, and we could do naught else."

"The Lord?" Endecott demanded incredulously. "I vow 'twas Satan!" and he hurried them to prison.

Of course the men refused to work, so they were starved for three days. Thus does the governor vie with John Norton in putting down this morbid fear of the Devil by relentlessly hounding our dear friends.

Arriving in Boston our marchers immediately sought a hearing from the governor. He listened impatiently for some moments to the men, but when Catharine—a woman—dared to question his judgment and that of the court, he could restrain himself no longer.

"Madam!" he thundered, "the duties of your sex do not include lecturing the governor and the general court of Massachusetts! Away with you to gaol, where a term of confinement may recall to you your proper place in life! And if you come here again, we are likely to hang you!"

But Catharine is not one to be cowed by abusive language. She spoke up sturdily. "When God calls us, we must come, though it be to certain death; for although life is dear to us, God's will and the life eternal are dearer still."

Yet 'twas the governor who had the last word. "And we shall be as ready to take away your lives, as you shall be to lay them down," he said ominously.

The guards then hurried this respectable, prosperous, elderly mother of nine off to a dark, dank dungeon for a few days, before she could contaminate other women, or even men, with her radical ideas on religion and deportment.

What shocking news has reached us now! 'Though my eyes are dry, the sobbing of my heart cannot be stilled; my soul cries out against this monstrous deed, and indignation's flame burns fiercely in my breast: Our dear friends have been cruelly mutilated by those malicious Boston butchers!

Protesting the court's sentence, Christopher requested a delay so that he might appeal to England. Besides, the angry townspeople demanded a sentence less stringent than ear-cropping. The crafty governor pretended to temporize. Then one dark night he secretly ordered the executioner to proceed.

When it was done and the warm blood coursed down their shirts, the governor mockingly inquired, "What say you now, vile wretches? Do you repent? Or do you wish more chastizing?"

"We suffer this loss joyfully," they said, "and will gladly give up all the parts of our body if the Lord require it. Moreover, we pray the Lord to forgive any who have joined in this cruelty from ignorance. But we warn those who shed our blood from malice that on the Judgment day our blood shall be upon their heads and our suffering upon their consciences, and they shall faint under the burden of this crime."

The same night they were whipped in their cell and left, torn and bleeding, to live or die; and if they lived, 'twas only with the expectation of more beatings during their term of confinement.

When news of this barbarous act leaked out, Catharine and other Friends marched to the gaol. A large crowd of sympathizers gathered as she prayed at the men's window. Then she turned to the crowd.

"What manner of men are these officials?" she cried. "Whence comes their authority for such foul deeds? From Jesus?" (Cries of "No! No!") "Does it come from you?" ("No!") "Then let us act! We cannot replace the severed ears. But we can see that this never happens again. Who will go with us to the governor?" A chorus of "I will!" swelled from the angry crowd. Quickly they stood aside to let Friends lead the way.

At that moment, however, the mounted guard clattered down the lane, laying about vigorously with their pike-staves and shouting, "Disperse! Disperse!" Several unresisting Friends fell to the ground, and one or two guardsmen were unhorsed by the excited marchers. Dashing up to Catharine, the captain seized her roughly and hoisted her to his saddle.

"Go home at once!" he bellowed. "Clear the area instantly, or this woman will be charged with rebellion, sedition, and inciting to riot, and will surely hang! Be off!"

He glared fiercely about him while his horse reared and plunged. And so the flailing hooves, the heavy cudgels, and the vicious threats subdued the defenseless people and they moved sullenly away. Catharine and other Friends were prodded and kicked into the gaol, and she was given ten lashes for her outspoken protest.

All hereabouts, Quakers and Baptists alike, are incensed at this dastardly treatment, but no one has any clear plan of action. Roger Williams, although heartily disagreeing with Quaker tenets and practices, has written to John Clarke to implore protection and liberty of conscience of the protector, but Oliver Cromwell has died and his son is but a weak substitute for the forceful, independent father.

Newport—1658

[*Sixth month*]

However bracing John considers our salty breezes and sea air, their effect on older constitutions is not so rapid, and I am only now strong enough to resume some limited preaching. I fear my witness in Boston must be postponed until the spring.

Catharine has returned home to the loving care of her family and is convalescing. Richard Scott is furious at the Boston officials and has attempted to retaliate by curtailing our trade with them. But although he has many friends and sympathizers on the island, they are not quite willing to forego the clinking coins and the full stomach just for conscience' sake.

John Rous's father, a wealthy sugar-planter in Barbados and one of the first Quakers there, heard of his son's horrible punishment, and is conferring with his close friend, the island governor, on possible reprisals.

Lawrence and Cassandra Southwick remain in Boston, constantly fined and otherwise harried. All their money is now gone, and they exist through secret donations of money and food. Lately they have ceased to attend church services, believing it wrong for anyone to be required to attend a church not of his own faith. Well, their property will go next; then they and the children must surely leave.

A horrible thought occurs to me: If Christian ministers can act so venomously toward fellow Christians, what manner of treatment would they reserve for the fifteen families of Jews recently arrived in Newport?

[*Eighth month*]

Our dear friend John Copeland has joined us again, but in very sad condition; Christopher of course is with the Scotts. 'Tis a marvel to me how these men, young and stalwart though they be, can endure such terrible physical punishment and retain an unshakable spirit. They are indeed the stuff of martyrs. They do confess, however, that their feelings toward their persecutors are not so kind as they would wish.

"I tried at first to remember that they are God's children too," John said, "but they only appear now like jungle animals, tearing and rending indiscriminately, without reason or any other human qualities. They are as stubborn as we are, in the pursuit of their faith. I wonder, though, how long they would remain true if *their* ears were cropped, and *their* backs were bared to the lash."

" 'Tis an interesting, but idle speculation," I replied, "for their malignant powers know no bounds. Mr. Norton himself. . ."

"Ah, yes," said John with a wry smile, " 'the babbling Pharisee,' as John Rous calls him."

"What is Norton like now?" I asked. "He was away from Boston when I was there."

"He is a dark and melancholy man, in appearance as well as spirit, brilliant, witty at times, yet pursued by fear. His only purpose in life is to defeat the Devil in hand-to-hand combat. To this end, any and all means are justified, and his greatest disciple is old John Endecott.

"Death itself has now become his weapon. At the latest general court a new Quaker law was introduced. The magistrates and officers passed it quickly, but the freemen voted it down—eleven for, fifteen against. Of these latter, one fell sick the next day and two were intimidated. So when the matter came up again several days later under Mr. Norton's personal direction, the vote was changed—thirteen for, twelve against. Now anyone convicted of being a Quaker may be banished and, if he come again, may be put to death.

"Norton's old crony, John Wilson, concurred in the law, crying, 'I would carry burning coals in one hand and flaming fagots in the other, to burn all the Quakers in the world. Hang them! or else . . .' and, leering horribly, he drew his finger significantly across his throat. Endecott has also recommended that like measures be adopted by the United Colonies committee."

John fell silent. "This law cannot be allowed to stand," he said at last. "It must be tested, and there are those of us who will not hesitate to do it."

"But not thou and Christopher and John," I cried. "You have all suffered more than enough!"

"In the spring," he murmured, and slowly set off for the beach.

[*Ninth month*]

Christopher and the two Johns have started south for Virginia and Maryland. William Robinson and Robert Hodgson will join them for the winter. Before leaving, Christopher purchased fifty acres of land here in Newport, and also prevailed on Roger Williams to sell him the Isle of Patience in the bay. Evidently he intends to settle here after his marriage rather than at Providence, and I doubt not Roger Williams is delighted to have this zealous Quaker as far from him as possible. Young Patience Scott rode over with him for the transaction. Though still a mere child, she shows wisdom and understanding beyond her years and a real talent for speaking. She says all her brothers and sisters have become Friends too.

I am disappointed that Will and Sam and Charlie do not join us, but if, after all I and others have said, they do not know in their hearts that our way is their way, I must make the best of it. For "God loveth a cheerful giver," and a grudging acceptance is worse than none.

Dear William Brend, one of the first to be banished under the Death law and now living in Providence, wrote a most inspiring message to our meeting recently:

"I testify, as the Lord's witness, that all the beatings, imprisonings, and threats inflicted on me had no more effect in diverting me from God's will than if I had been chained by the silkworm's thread."

Lawrence and Cassandra Southwick are also in Providence, having lost all their property and been banished from Boston; but the boy and girl remain there under the care of Friends.

[*Tenth month*]

Terrible news concerning the young Southwick children: True to their faith they refused to attend Boston church, and for this they were fined heavily. As they had no money, however, they were cast—mere babes—into prison and now await the judgment of Third month court.

[*Eleventh month*]

Another sweet grandbaby to hold in my arms! She has Mary's fair complexion and Tom's straight nose and determined chin. She sleeps all night and most of the day, bestows her smiles and gurgles liberally and impartially, and has enslaved us all with her charms. Much as I loved my own babies, I love this one even more; and Will's first thought on entering the house is to shuffle to her cradle to see if she's awake, but, of course, if she is, she's not in the cradle but being fondled and dandled and kissed and hugged by everybody.

Newport—1658

Mary has not yet regained her strength, and Will's rheumatism is worse in the cold weather, so I must be content with nursing my family and preaching locally; but in the spring I shall definitely have to range farther afield.

[*Twelfth month*]

A letter from Christopher informs us that he and William Robinson and my English friend, Marmaduke Stevenson, recently arrived from Barbados, will shortly set out for the North. All Friends who can will come together at Providence in Second month for a general meeting to plan any further manner in which we may witness to our living faith.

1659

[*Second month*]

How good it was to see old friends at general meeting and meet the new ones! A large number gathered in Providence, most of us staying in private homes but a few at Roger Mowry's tavern. Roger Williams eyed these latter most suspiciously, but they in no way disturbed the prayer meeting he held there, and so he was then most affable to them.

Meeting consisted largely of reports on Friends' activities and accomplishments both in this country and abroad. In old England Friends now number in the thousands; here we are numbered only in the hundreds. But we can not be discouraged: For as long as tyranny of body, or custom, or mind exists, there will be brave men to resist; but as soon as men learn to hearken to the divine voice within, these tyrannies will cease to be.

Our plan is to continue to spread the gospel as revealed to us throughout the colonies. We shall concentrate our energies and resources particularly in the North, where every decent feeling has been flouted, where freedom is a myth and justice a mockery. Christopher, William Robinson, and Marmaduke Stevenson will be the first to go. They take with them Patience Scott, only eleven now; but she has understanding and ability far beyond her years.

[*Third month*]

Is there no limit to this madness? Are there no bounds at all of human decency which those venomous ministers will recognize? They seem determined to wring the last drop of compassion from their bodies as well as the last drop of blood from ours, and crush the seed of love and righteousness which God has planted in their hearts.

O what a dry and barren bed has this seed! Those hearts are as hard as the rocky fields at Duxbury, those minds as narrow as Newport's Purgatory, where the churning waters rush in among the cliffs with tumultuous force. But as the salty waters are sucked out of the fissure with a resounding boom, so shall the waters of their iniquity be drained from them at the clap of Judgment, and they shall stand empty and hollow, for they are wicked, they are evil, they have perverted the Lord's Word to their own ends, and their brutal crimes against us shall be counted and written down, and neither howls of rage nor tearful pleas of "duty" done shall be heard.

Nay, what they have sown, they shall reap, and the Lord shall judge them even as they have judged us. And not one voice shall intercede for them—nay, not their closest followers—, for they have ordered Daniel and Provided Southwick sold into slavery!

"Numerous and strong protests to Governor Endecott from shocked Christians throughout the North have not prevailed on him to release Daniel and Provided," our messenger reported to Friends recently. "'Tis only the lack of a willing—and unscrupulous—captain which has saved them from being transported to Barbados. For while some men deal openly in the *black* slave trade, none has yet had courage to trade in *white* babies!"

"Come, Friends," said Will Coddington in his pompous, yet sincere way, "let us donate what money we can spare to pay the fine and secure the children's release." He slipped several coins into his hat and passed it around. Later, when he thought no one was looking, he added several more for the messenger to take to Boston.

Our own dear little ones have suffered much with the red rash and fever these past few weeks, and Mary and I have had our hands full nursing them and attending to our usual duties. I hope to leave for Boston as soon as they are well.

[*Fourth month*]

Our messenger reports that Friends reached Boston and Salem safely and preached some weeks without hindrance. "Eventually, however," he said, "they were all arrested except Patience. She was considered too young to bother with. But she is a plucky girl, and was, no doubt, a little nettled too at being ignored. So up she spoke and protested vigorously against the sentence of whipping and banishment for the men. The governor was certainly not going to allow a young maid to reprove him before the court with impunity. Now she too has been imprisoned but her sentence is only a small fine. Poor Christopher!" he concluded, "If they do not hang him, they will certainly flay him to death!"

Our children continue to catch every possible disease, it seems, but perhaps 'tis better for them to have everything all at once and get it over, though I cannot help chafing at these forced changes of my plans. "All in good time, my dear," says Will contentedly, but patience was never one of my outstanding virtues.

[*Fifth month*]

William Robinson and Marmaduke have returned to Lynn and Salem, where they preach occasionally in private homes, but more often in the fields and woods, as their friends insist 'tis safer for all. Christopher has gone farther north. His endurance and persistence are truly remarkable.

[*Sixth month*]

Once again our dear friends have been arrested. What hope is there now for them? 'Tis all very well for us to sit here and urge them to go out and test this wicked law, but now that they face certain death, I feel serious misgivings concerning my own part in this matter. My intentions were good, but what have I accomplished? How have I furthered our cause? Was I wrong to remain here where duty seemed to lie?

But it is too late for regrets. Now it is time for action: Catharine and Richard Scott are not well; therefore it is up to me to go to Boston and bring Patience home, and at the same time test this vile law anew. If a young girl can brave the dangers of the lion's den, surely a mature woman can also look the beast in the eye.

Will is writing a letter to the governor which I am to take. I leave tomorrow.

Boston

How the city has grown even in the two years since last I was here; it is really getting rather cluttered with all the new shops and houses. And such elegant houses, too!

Quite a few now are brick; I can remember when Will Coddington's was the only brick house. The stiff blue Boston weed, as they call it here, still blooms profusely in yards and meadows, and the stately elms along the common give welcome shade to cows and men alike.

Captain Edward Hutchinson, at great danger to himself and his family, has taken me in for the short time I shall be here. When I expressed concern for his safety, he smiled wryly and said, "I doubt if even Governor Endecott will be so rash as to arrest a captain of the artillery, particularly one who can rattle a few gold pieces as well as a sword." I fervently pray he is right.

The day I set out to visit the governor, Edward wished to accompany me, but I convinced him 'twould be foolish to take any further risk. Stepping briskly down the walk, I had no sooner turned into the street when two guardsmen appeared, seized my arms, and hurried me to gaol. Once inside I embraced Patience warmly and reassured myself that her pale and emaciated appearance betokened no serious illness but only a lack of sunlight, fresh air, good food, and love, all of which would shortly be supplied in full measure.

On speaking also with our other dear friends in prison, I found them eager to be released, yet adamant in their determination to go on preaching here. It was a hard decision for me: In gaol they were uncomfortable, but safe; freed, they would be in mortal danger. Yet was it really my decision to make? If God had called them to preach—even unto death—, how could I prevent them? And so, reluctantly, I left the money for their fines—along with my heartfelt prayers—and prepared to confront the governor the next day.

With one guard in front and one behind, Patience and I set out next day for Endecott's house. Along the way one or two old friends clasped my hand in warm greeting, and a number of strangers passed by with only a curious glance at our sober gowns and ribbonless bonnets. A few old acquaintances drew back in obvious horror and quickly turned away as we approached. Their action puzzled me until I overheard excited whispers of, "The witch! 'Tis she of the monstrous birth!" My heart ached to think that this terrible gossip had survived so long; but then I thought, 'twas only natural in the suspicious, malignant atmosphere of Boston. We walked rapidly on and at last turned in at the governor's gate.

Up the little brick path we strode, past the sundial in the midst of formal flower beds (there is no evil, then, in flowers, Governor?), up the few steps to the oak door with its heavy brass knocker.

A servant in bright livery led us to a waiting room, where I sank down gratefully on the edge of a chair. A door opened somewhere and I could hear the governor's high voice fondly advising a grandchild that certain unpleasant experiences were bound to occur if he persisted in pulling the cat's tail (thou dost not look upon all little children as evil monsters, Governor?). Footsteps approached. I arose. The governor, carrying an indignant tabby whom he soothed gently, stepped smiling into the room.

As he recognized me, his eyes widened, then narrowed; his pleasant smile became a scowl. "What, Mistress Dyer!" he exclaimed, dropping the cat abruptly and advancing toward me. "Here again! You are not welcome in this colony, as you well know. I thought we made this clear at the time of your last visit, and doubly so in recent months." His voice was tight with scorn and anger.

"I am fully aware of thy barbarous laws, John Endecott,"

I said. "My friends have suffered often enough because of them."

"Yet you dare to enter this town, this house, with your poisonous tongue? Do you care nothing for your skin—or will the Devil replace it for you after we have flayed it?"

"I do not fear thy lash," I said disdainfully (though not quite truthfully). "Though thy minions flog me, brand me, hang me, I have yet a free soul which thou canst not touch. And my strength cometh not from the Devil, but from God, my Protector, and the Father of us all."

"God is not the father of witches and heretics," he screamed.

"The Father of us all," I repeated firmly. "Wilt thou examine my body for witch marks?" I made to undo my kerchief. He shrank back; I advanced. "Wilt thou have the church examine me for heresy? Thou knowest no heresy hath been proven against us. But stop, I did not come to preach or argue. I have come to pay the fine of a wicked, depraved criminal, a fearsome danger to the community. I speak of this child, Patience Scott."

"Oh, aye," he said with a rather ashamed air. "But we could not allow her to criticize our actions publicly. It is not seemly for a child—still less a girl child—to question her elders. We only put her in gaol so she would not infect the other children with her pernicious views."

"Indeed? And if thy grandchild were sick of an infectious disease, thou wouldst of course shut her in a dark, damp cell without straw to lie on, and starve her, and deny her any attendant to nurse her?"

"Well, but the cases are not the . . . ," he stammered.

"Take thy gold, John Endecott, and give me the child. For she is dearer to us than any number of lifeless, soulless coins!" I held out a small bag to him. He reached for it eagerly, then drew back as if afraid some witchery might occur. Finally he snatched it from me and retreated behind his desk. Summoning his secretary, he ordered a notice of banishment for me, and a release for both of us.

"You are now formally banished from this colony upon pain of death," he growled and, thrusting the papers at me, called for the servant to show me out. "Good day, Mistress Dyer," he said, resuming his threatening attitude. "Take the child and leave Boston immediately. And if you are so foolish as to come here again, we shall not spare you."

"Dost thou call thy Maker foolish, John Endecott?" I said sharply. "For it is he who hath led me here; and if it be his will that I come again, here will I come." So saying, I laid Will's letter on the desk, took Patience by the hand, and left the house.

Newport

Our trip was quickly made, Patience deposited within the joyous arms of her family, and I reunited with mine. Yet I am conscious of a voice within which tells me tenderly, but insistently, that my part has not been fully played; and I await a call to further action. In the meantime I rejoice at this small chance to witness for my God.

Will says his letter accused the Boston authorities of persecuting more people in one year than England's worst bishops did in seven. Dear man, he still has fire and spirit left, but 'tis a lucky thing I did not give Endecott the letter until we were about to leave!

[*Seventh month*]

How poignantly the season's beauty moves me, how touchingly the cry of Sam's new son. My ears catch every slightest whisper, my eyes see every tiny mite. The goldenrod and pimpernel stand vividly against the darkening sky; the ash and maple splash their brilliant hues amongst the somber pines. My senses are somehow heightened, sharpened: the sights, the sounds, the smells. Oh, how keenly do I smell the autumn leaves, their earthy dampness in the wood, or acrid burning in the field. How sharp the salty tang of ocean breeze, how sweet the plump red fruit, the new-mown hay, a baby's breath; the pungent odor of the herds, of new-made shoes, of fish and clams, and coals upon the hearth; how heavenly the smell of fresh-washed clothes, how savory the baking bread, the simmering stew.

All sights are mine, all sounds are mine, all smells are mine. For my days on earth are numbered now, and judgment's close at hand. Already Friends are gathering in Boston town, not to protest, but to hearten and inspire, for Christopher Holder lies again in gaol and I must join him soon.

[*Eighth month*] *Boston*

Catharine Scott being still unwell, her daughter Mary and a young Friend, Hope Clifton, accompanied our group here as representatives from Providence. The Southwick children follow with Robert Harper and Nicholas Upsal, and others also are on the way.

Of the parting with my loved ones I shall not write, for my heart is still too close to tears, and my strength must be conserved for the greater trials ahead.

Tomorrow I shall visit Christopher.

The Lion's Den

Clutching the bag with my journal and clean linen in it, I stepped forth this morning with a show of bravery I really did not feel. My heart pounded furiously as we turned into the street, and I dared not look the others in the face. The two girls said nothing but walked quietly.

"How empty the streets are!" I said at last.

"Aye," said Mary, " 'tis strange indeed. 'Tis probably the threat of rain which keeps everyone indoors," —for gloomy, gray clouds hung low overhead.

We abandoned any further attempts at conversation and continued on in silence until we reached the gaol. Rapping on the window bars with a stick and calling Christopher's name, we finally found his cell. Greatly astonished, he peered out. "What are ye doing here, Friends? Make haste away! This dismal dungeon is no place for young maidens. Nor for thee, Mary Dyer. Thou'rt in mortal danger!"

"No more than thou art, young man," I declared. "And we've come to keep thee company, not to run away."

Christopher shook his head in dismay.

"It's no use arguing," said Hope stoutly. "We'll not leave until thou dost."

At this moment the gaoler rushed around the corner, a guard close behind. "Seize them!" he cried. "Talk to the prisoner, will you? And Quakers too! Arrest them all! I'll gladly provide suitable accommodations if that's what you desire!"

Unresisting, we submitted to the men's angry shoving and shortly were thrust into a cell, while the guard dashed off to inform the governor then sitting in general court.

"Well, friends, this will be our dwelling place for some time," I remarked. "Let us see if any improvements have been made since I was here last. At least 'tis light inside."

The girls poked into all the corners but could find no benches or straw, and so we disposed ourselves as comfortably as we could on the hard, stone floor.

Shortly thereafter we heard the gaoler banging noisily outside our window. Investigating, the girls cried in anguish, "Oh, he is boarding it up! We shall be left in total darkness."

"Come, my dears," I chided. "There are worse things than darkness. Besides, 'twill provide a wonderful atmosphere for our prayers. Naught can then distract us."

As it turned out, however, the gaoler was a careless fellow, who left a few chinks for the sun's weak rays to enter, and thus we were immensely cheered.

Two days later

The noise of a great crowd and the clanking of chains this morning brought the girls rushing to the window, eager for any event to break the monotony of this wretched existence. Peeping through the window cracks, they supplied me excitedly with details.

"The crowd is angry and unruly."

"The horse guard have some difficulty getting through."

"Oh, here come the prisoners!"

"Oh, see the heavy chains. They must be dangerous men indeed. They are simply loaded with irons."

"But look! They're wearing Quaker hats!"

"Let me see!" I cried and, hurrying up, looked out. "Why, 'tis Marmaduke, and William Robinson. Alas, I fear these chains betoken grievous portents, for Christopher was not so manacled when last conducted here." Turning slowly, I sat down to adjust my thoughts to this ominous sight.

I find that darkness, quiet, fasting, and prayer have all combined to relieve my body of its former nervousness: each time I pray, the world is shut out more easily, and my soul centers more quickly on the Lord. Thus am I now quite calm and content, sure of my fate, certain I shall have the strength to do my part to the Lord's glory.

Later the young guard rapped busily on the window-boarding, and the girls flew over in dismay.

"Thou'rt not stuffing the chinks, art thou?" Hope pleaded.

"I really ought to," he replied warily.

"Oh, please, do let us have this bit of sun and air," she said, applying a bright blue eye to the opening. She started back as a soft brown eye gazed in at her, then smothered a hysterical giggle. They carried on a most un-Quakerly, but quite normal maid-and-man conversation for some time. He said his name was Edward Wanton; he was sure there was no great harm in us; he clucked sympathetically when told Mary and Christopher were betrothed, and finally promised to tell him she was well and thought of him constantly.

This exchange cheered the girls immeasurably; and though my own situation allowed no such levity, I was glad for their sakes.

Later still Edward returned with an ardent message from Christopher and a reassuring one from William and Marmaduke: They had not been ill treated and had been relieved of their irons; we were all to go before the court tomorrow; a number of other Friends had arrived and would walk with us to the court.

The girls thanked Edward sweetly while he stammered bashfully, and we all rejoiced at having found a friend within the lion's den.

Next day

The gaoler, surly as ever but mindful of our appearance in court, allowed us a jug of cold water to cleanse ourselves and left the door open a bit so we could see; and after forcing the cold, lumpy porridge down our reluctant throats to protesting stomachs, we were herded into the street to join the men. We clasped hands eagerly and murmured words of encouragement to one another. Then Captain Wanton stepped forward with a great show of military correctness, and, speaking in a loud, officious manner (but winking furtively), he ordered the other soldiers to surround us and proceed.

A number of persons stood quietly, gazing curiously at us as we passed. We heard a few angry shouts, but a number of sympathetic ones, too. From time to time an out-of-town Friend left the crowd to join us.

As Alice Cowland stepped in behind us, Hope asked innocently, "What is that linen on thine arm, Alice?"

" 'Tis Christopher's shroud," she replied in a low voice.

But Mary heard, and faltered. We tightened our arms about her, and though dreadfully pale, she managed to continue.

At last we reached the meetinghouse and entered. The magistrates and assistants were seated on one side, the freemen on the other; Governor Endecott and his deputy occupied chairs on the low platform, where they glared at us with obvious distaste. Herded upon the platform, we ranged ourselves opposite them and stared back resolutely.

"You know the law which forbids your sect from coming among us," said the governor in his most menacing tones. "Why then do you persist in annoying us and laying yourselves open to great bodily harm and even death?"

"We are sent by God to look your bloody laws in the face," replied Christopher. "We fear neither threats, nor injury, nor death, and we shall resist your evil persecutions with all the strength God grants us."

John Norton sprang to his feet. "Your strength comes

from Satan himself, but all the powers of hell shall not prevail against us! We shall yet frustrate your wicked end."

"Thy end shall be frustrated," I said sharply, "if thou thinkest to keep us from coming among you. Yea, verily, the Lord hath a great work here among you, for which we have suffered all this while, and for which we desire to to suffer as long as need be."

"Be silent, woman!" Norton said contemptuously. "Let the men speak."

At this rude remark our male friends turned toward me and nodded with one accord as Marmaduke said mildly, "We believe God speaks to man and woman both, and each has equal right to speak and be heard. Mary Dyer may speak for us if she will."

"We come among you," I said, "with no intention to harm or to disrupt—nay, we seek to further peace and understanding. We are innocent of any wrong-doing. But we must obey the Lord's will, and he has called us to witness his truth in all places to all men. Where truth be suppressed, or liberty of conscience denied, we can do naught but protest, for all men must be free to serve the Lord as they are called. And if you silence us, still others will come to cry against your wicked laws."

However, all our pleas for tolerance were unavailing, and we were speedily convicted under the banishment law. The Puritans then fell to wrangling among themselves as to whether it was really wise to inflict the death penalty and incur the displeasure of the general population, who much opposed it, or whether there were recourses more effective and advisable. However, court adjourned for the day without reaching a decision.

We returned to the prison, a solemn, silent group; for though the possibility of death weighed heavily on our hearts, we all realized that an even more momentous decision lies before the court. In earlier ages Christian had murdered Turk, Catholic had murdered Jew—all for the glory of God. Will Puritans now continue the slaughter of God's children, or will they turn aside into the paths of peace? Our lives are not important—others will take our place; but if the priests pursue their obstinate course, they blight the divine seed within them, they lose their own soul, they destroy the souls of countless numbers who mistakenly follow after them. Many souls will come to judgment on the morrow: Though they inhabit the flesh for scores of years to come, their good works will not erase tomorrow's deeds.

My own mind is at ease: I have heeded the voice of the Lord, I have run the race, I have accomplished the task; I have looked into Death's frightful eyes and faced him down; and, if it please God, I shall step with a firm foot and a faithful heart out of the temporal life into the life eternal.

The guard knocks, we must prepare. A handclasp all 'round, a silent prayer—then we must attend upon the court and await its pleasure.

The court's pleasure is death. So be it. Upon their heads be the shame; upon their heads fall the wrath of the nation; upon their heads come the judgment of a just God. We joyfully accept the consequences of our actions. Let them do likewise.

As for the proceedings this morn, we listened quietly to Governor Endecott's vituperative sermon detailing to the court the menace we Quakers present to the community; we listened silently while he worked up to a frenzied rage to justify his morbid fears; we noted the occasional glances toward Mr. Norton and Mr. Wilson and the encouraging nods they returned; we listened stoically as the court voted us guilty by a narrow margin.

Pausing at last for breath, the governor then advanced several paces toward us. We stepped forward. A great hush fell upon all the people. Lifting an admonitory finger, Endecott proclaimed the sentence in a stifled voice.

"We have not desired your death. On the contrary, we have attempted in the past to spare your lives. But since no warning, no punishment has prevailed over your stubborn madness, we now have no choice but to carry out the law. Mary Dyer, William Robinson, Marmaduke Stevenson: you shall go hence, to the place whence you came, and thence to the place of execution, and there be hanged until you be dead."

Many of the assembly were too stunned to speak; they could only gape at one another. The silence thickened, horror grew. Stepping forward, I looked John Endecott straight in the eye.

"The will of the Lord be done." As the sudden fear started into his eyes, a great warmth and power surged into my heart. I turned to the meeting. Stretching forth my hands to include them all, I exclaimed fervently, "The will of the Lord be done. Yea, and joyfully I go."

There was a moment more of silence, then John Winthrop, Jr., a visitor to the court, sprang to his feet. "No!" he cried. "I beg the court—I will go down on bended knee—, do not carry out this harsh sentence! Imprison these people, cast them out. But, for the love of Jesus Christ, do not kill them!"

"Silence!" cried Mr. Norton. "You are not governor here."

"Thank God I am not," replied Winthrop. "Massachusetts knows Connecticut has no room for Quakers within her bounds. But you go too far. This sentence can only bring shame upon you."

"The Devil may take Connecticut!" snarled Wilson. "He shall not have Boston."

"Asylum! I offer them all asylum at my own expense." 'Twas the governor of Acadia and Nova Scotia.

A sharp poke in the ribs from John Norton reminded Endecott of his duty, and he quickly forestalled any further sympathetic action. "The court has decreed they shall hang in eight days," he said in a quavering voice, "and hang they shall! Court is adjourned. Take the prisoners away."

The guard immediately removed us, but the uproar continued. The news spread quickly, and before we had reached the gaol a sympathetic crowd gathered and streamed after us, pushing and shouting at the pikemen, who were hard put to defend themselves. Inside we listened in amazement as the crowd battered at our window-boarding and sought to enter and release us. As the boarding gave way, we were hurried to a lower dungeon without windows. The men were soon thrust into an adjacent cell, and as the oaken door was left open with only the iron grating to confine us, we were able to speak with them and offer, as well as receive, words of comfort and cheer.

For though Marmaduke, William, and I remained uplifted and unafraid, our younger, untried friends occasionally gave way to grief and despair as the horror of the coming event impressed itself upon them.

As we reassured them that God had not deserted us but was even then supporting us with his love and kindness, and that eventually his will would triumph over all evil and soften even the hardest heart, we wondered what

Christopher's fate would be. The rest of our friends would be beaten, probably; banished, certainly. But what of him who already has been twice banished on pain of death? This fawning, frightened governor must fear the wrath of Christopher's highly placed and wealthy relations in England. The lad himself is nearly frantic at his failure to receive our sentence also.

But Mary Scott rejoices quietly, and I do likewise. We older three have enjoyed the best of life and suffered the worst; we have used our small store of talents in the Lord's service, we have kept the faith. But now the younger ones, those given more talents, must carry on; and Christopher must live, so that others shall not die.

Enough—I have still some influence in this land and highly placed friends myself. Perhaps the court can be persuaded to take my life and spare my friends. What shall I write in this appeal?

"In love and meekness I beseech you to repeal these cruel laws, to stay this wicked sentence. 'Though you have harmed us grievously in the past, no life has been lost. But now, if you shed our innocent blood, you will kill not only our bodies, but your infinitely more precious souls. For the wages of sin is death, and 'tis a heinous sin indeed to kill your fellowmen, children of God like you, who only seek to preach his Word. Relent, I beg you; repent, I implore you; for if you persist, you will surely feel God's heavy hand on Judgment day.

"But if one of us must die that others may live, let me be the one; for if my life were freely granted by you, I could not accept it so long as my sisters suffered and my brothers died. For what is life compared with the witness to the truth?

"Therefore let the light of Christ with its loving warmth

soften your hearts; and let his light bring your minds out of darkness to freedom and glory; for his is the way to everlasting life, but the way of the devil is death. . . ."

The ministers visit us daily and urge us to recant but that we shall never do. God himself has spoken to us and led us here, and to deny him now would be a sin more heinous than that which the priests contemplate. Our spirits remain high; the younger ones among us now accept what is to be and thereby strengthen their own resolve to carry on the work. William and Marmaduke have both written letters to be distributed among Friends as their last testimony; but I shall content myself with the appeal for their freedom.

Willie has come! My joy at seeing him, however, is tempered by his lack of understanding. He comes, not to lend his strength, but to urge me to recant, to save my own poor life while others die. I have told him, "Where *one* is coerced, *none* is free. While these barbarous and restrictive laws remain, I cannot be content to be safe. Nor shouldst thou either." And at last he admitted this is true.

The guard about the gaol has been increased, for the people are incensed against this law and the severe penalty.

Friends kept vigil with Willie and me all last night. Now the day is at hand. I have prayed and fasted. I am ready to meet my Lord. This day shall I be with him in Paradise.

[*Ninth month*] *Newport*

Paradise, did I write? Nay, though this fair island has often seemed a paradise to me, it is now a hell, a place of unutterable anguish, of constant torment. The good wishes of my friends are a burden, the embraces of my family a reproach: For my two beloved friends are dead—dead in the cause of the freedom we all longed for—, while I yet live.

Live for what? I was ready to die, I desired it; but instead I was freed. Why did I fail, where was my mistake? My brain is in turmoil, it grows weary of seeking an answer, but an answer must be found. Was there some fault in me? Or was it all the work of man, rather than of God? How I should like to believe that! I must review again those sad and mournful hours. . . .

On the fateful morn we bade our friends a restrained yet joyous farewell. As we came out of the darkness into the chill, gloomy day, William lifted his arms radiantly toward the clamoring crowd and began to speak; but the gaoler, whose heart is as stony as his prison walls, rushed forward and cuffed him vigorously until Captain Wanton intervened.

His face pale and eyes averted, Edward placed me between William and Marmaduke and adjusted their chains. Captain Oliver looked on with a sneer.

"Are you not ashamed to walk between two young men in public, Mistress Dyer?" he said. "Are you not saddened now by your rash actions and theirs?"

I clasped my friends' hands and answered proudly, "It is an hour of the greatest joy I can experience in this world. No eye can see, no ear can hear, no tongue can speak, no heart can understand the sweet incomes and refreshings of the spirit of the Lord which I now enjoy."

Disconcerted, he nodded to the drummers; they lifted their sticks, and he gave the order to proceed. Two hundred soldiers, with a vast array of arms, pressed close about us. We could not speak, we could not sing, the noise of the drums was so great. The crowd, too, was noisy and violent, restrained with difficulty from rioting. Hundreds of visitors augmented the townsmen—some to witness, some to try to prevent this day's monstrous deed; and the horses reared and plunged, and neighed shrilly in alarm.

As we reached the governor's house, he and the magistrates fell in before us. 'Twas only a short, quick mile to the common—through the streets, over the bridge, up the slight slopes. Then we had reached the great elm; and there the priests awaited us, beside an ugly pit. The governor joined them.

Clad in their black garments, the officials of church and state presented an ominous appearance: Mr. Norton's face was stern, his eyes blazed with malice; yet fear lurked beneath the black brows and in the grim visage. John Wilson, on the other hand, capered about mocking the men because they steadfastly retained their hats in the presence of the authorities.

William was led first to the ladder. When he had mounted, his hands were bound behind him, his eyes covered, and the rope placed about his throat.

Governor Endecott spoke. "Is there anything you wish to say before sentence is carried out?"

William turned his face toward the quiet, expectant multitude. In a firm, loud voice he said, "I suffer for Christ, in whom I have lived, and for whom I die."

"You have lived for the Devil!" railed Wilson. "Now may he take you to the burning pits of hell!"

The executioner grasped the wood.

"God keep thee, friend," I murmured, and watched him die. A woman shrieked, another fell senseless. The crowd began to mutter.

William's body still swung slowly as Marmaduke stepped forward.

The governor glanced round nervously and moistened

his lips. "Have you anything to say before sentence is carried out?"

Marmaduke spoke up clearly. "Be it known unto all this day that we suffer not as evildoers, but for conscience' sake."

"A pretty conscience," scoffed Wilson, "which seeks to pull down and destroy both church and state alike. But you shall not succeed, you accursed servants of Satan! We will pry you from the slimy stones, we will harry you from your dark lairs, we will trap you with the nets of righteousness and hang you till your souls flee again to Lucifer!"

Marmaduke lifted his head proudly.

"God keep thee, friend," I murmured, and watched him die.

The crowd began to press forward, and angry shouts burst forth: "Enough!" "An end to this!" "This is not justice, this is murder!" A sudden clap of thunder startled us all.

"Interfere not!" commanded Norton with a gesture heavenward. "These damnable vipers must be crushed now, or the wrath of God will fall heavily on our heads!"

I took a deep breath and walked steadily toward the tree. Mounting the ladder, I permitted my limbs to be bound. Then John Wilson scurried forward.

"I did baptize your first-born," he cried, "and heard your husband promise that you would bring him up in the nurture and admonition of the Lord. But you began even then to consort with Satan and minister to him, and so you brought forth a monster for your next child. From that time forward you have gone from attempted witchery to outright heresy. Since I did not smite you then as I ought, let me make amends and do it now!" So saying, he flung his handkerchief in my face and angrily ordered the executioner to cover my eyes.

"Mary Dyer," the governor said, "we give you one last chance. If you promise to leave our colony and never return, we will remit the sentence and spare your life. Will you so promise?"

"Never!" I declared. "The Lord has commanded me to protest these laws. My life is in his hands. Do what you will."

He shrugged slightly and motioned to the executioner.

"Stop!" a voice cried, and a soldier burst from the crowd. Waving a paper, he plunged awkwardly toward us, hampered by boots and gun. "A reprieve!" he shouted.

I glanced down in surprise and dismay at Endecott, who was waiting impatiently. "How can this be?" I said. "A reprieve can come only from thee, and thou hast not given it."

He paid no attention to me, but snatched the paper from the soldier's hand. From the corner of my eye I saw Willie hurry forward. The governor raised a hand for silence and read aloud: "The General Court does hereby commute the sentence of Mary Dyer to banishment on pain of death, on condition that she leave this place within forty-eight hours. Otherwise the sentence will be carried out."

"But how is this possible?" I asked. "The court met some days ago and passed sentence, and my friends have died under that sentence."

"Do not stand there asking questions," he exclaimed impatiently. "Come down! We give you back your life."

"Come down, Mother!" cried Willie.

I heeded him not. "Do you then annul these cruel laws?"

"We annul no laws against heretics," snarled Norton. "Pull her down."

So the laws would stand, and men would continue to

die. 'Twas only a slight distaste for hanging women which allowed me to go free. I had no choice but to reject such terms. "My life is not accepted! For with wicked hands have you put two to death, which makes me to feel that the mercies of the wicked are cruelty. I rather choose to die than to live as from you, guilty of their innocent blood."

But though I protested and struggled, Willie pulled me quickly from the ladder, and, saying over his shoulder, "I bind myself to conduct her immediately from this colony," he hurried me toward the gaol, as the rain began to fall.

I looked back once. They were cutting my friends from the tree and casting them into the pit. Then the rain pelted down and the crowd massed behind us,—running, pushing, shouting—some enraged at my escape, others eager to be safe inside their homes. As we neared the gaol, we heard a sharp crack, and, looking back once more, saw the bridge slowly give way beneath the crowd, dumping officials and commoners, good and bad alike, into the muddy stream. Willie hurried me on, saying only, "They have rescuers enough. We must look to our own safety."

Reaching the gaol, he snatched up my bag, sprang onto his horse, and pulled me up behind. Four guards ranged themselves about us and we galloped off toward the boundary. Still dazed, dismayed, despondent, sodden, I could only cling to Willie dumbly as we sped through the storm, until at last our weary mounts plodded along the muddy streets of Newport and I tumbled into the arms of my loved ones. They tucked me quickly into a warm, soft bed. Then my dazed mind gave way to overwhelming grief, for I saw my dear friends lying dead in a cold, wet bed of dirt.

It was some weeks before I regained my strength and

health. During that time Will and I discussed the reprieve again and again. Perhaps he is right: It must have been planned in secret by the court and held in reserve. They never meant to hang me, only to threaten me into bowing to their wicked laws. If that is so, then God's plan for me has not altered; it has only been thwarted temporarily by evil men.

I did not watch my friends die for nothing. Unless the laws are changed, I shall go again to Boston.

[*Tenth month*]

Our other friends are straggling home now. The men each received fifteen lashes, the older women ten; the younger ones, like Alice, Hope, and Mary, were railed at for their foolishness and admonished. Christopher was banished again two days after William and Marmaduke died; and, discouraged at his seeming failure here, he set sail at once to use his influence in England to stop this madness. God grant they send us aid.

As for myself, my resolve weakens daily. The loving ties of home and hearth draw me farther from my duty, and I must leave at once if I am not to deny my Lord. I shall winter in Long Island.

1660

[*First month*] *Flushing*

Since the weather has turned mild, I have traveled from one end of the island to the other, circulating the letters of our dear friends and preaching not only God's Word but the cause of religious freedom also. For Governor Stuyvesant is a cruel, narrow man who persecutes Baptists and Quakers here as much as do the men to the north. At Hempstead Robert Hodgson was tortured and flogged, and here at Flushing Henry Townsend was imprisoned and fined, contrary to the charter. The citizens, outraged at this cruelty and tyranny, drew up what they called the "Flushing Remonstrance," pleading for religious tolerance. Of course some of the signers were punished, but they are sturdy, stubborn folk and will not be oppressed for long, particularly since their Dutch neighbors also assist their cause.

I am staying with John and Hannah Bowne and his father, Thomas. How my little ones would like to hear Thomas' story of how he killed a bear here once with nothing but his staff, which he thrust between the savage jaws and down into the eager throat.

Friends have no meetinghouse here and dare not meet in town, so they gather in the woods. Hannah says 'tis a lovely cool spot in summer, and I daresay she is right—it is certainly cool enough today.

[*Second month*] *Shelter Island*

I am growing impatient with the long winter. If I am to go to Boston, I want to be off. My spirit is restless and chafes at this enforced delay. My mind is filled with thoughts of Marmaduke and William, and my only desire now is to test their sacrifice. A poor word, sacrifice—it was no sacrifice for them to give their lives, nay, it was a joy; but they were offered up by the governor and ministers on the altar of Abraham and Isaac. These churchmen know not the Spirit of Christ, and I pity them; for they have the Word of God before them, yet they heed it not; they might live radiantly in Christ's love, yet they are wretched with fear. They shun the basic principle of Christian life—the Golden Rule; and they have forgotten the Beatitudes. Still, they may yet, like Paul, see the blinding light which reveals all things.

There! I am content now. God has guided my thoughts and my pen into more constructive channels, and I shall calmly and serenely await my call.

I shall not communicate with the family again. 'Tis better so, we have said enough farewells. Just a line or two for Nathaniel to send on afterward—something to keep them from mourning and from bitterness. . . .

"My dear husband and children, you know I do not leave you of my own choice. If I could choose, we should never be apart. But the Lord must be served, and I rejoice that he has called me, who have little talent or wisdom or power to this important task.

"So I beseech you always to remember that his arm sustains and comforts you, that love is the greatest good, and that in the end, his will shall prevail.

"God's greatest blessings be upon you, prays your loving wife and mother."

[*Third month*] *Providence*

John Taylor, Margaret Smith, and I rest here a few days before going on. John has guided us here from the island, and although we can easily make our way now by the Boston road, he insists upon going along. I shall not argue—it is good to have companions, for the road of life is often just as difficult on the smooth highways from town to town as on the wild and winding forest paths.

The Lion's Den

Once more I gaze upon these stony walls and watch the oaken door swing slowly shut on creaking hinges. This hovel is my home now for the brief time remaining to me. Gladly did I enter here, more gladly shall I leave; for though I came to plead against the law, repeal does not seem likely. If Marmaduke and William have died without effect, perhaps I too shall die in vain. But try I must—someone must try; and after me there will be others.

The court's action was much as we expected. John Endecott, scowling fiercely, began the proceedings.

"You are the same Mary Dyer that was here before?"

"I am."

"You confess yourself a Quaker, do you not?"

"I do."

"Then I find you guilty of breaking our law and sentence you to death by hanging."

"John Endecott, thou hast already put to death two of the Lord's witnesses. Wilt thou stain thy hands with the blood of yet a third?"

"Your blood is on your own head, not mine, and tomorrow morning at nine o'clock you shall join your friends."

I made one last attempt. "I have come in obedience to God's will to beseech thee to repeal this wicked law. But I tell thee truly that if thou persist, others will follow after me. Thou canst not kill them all."

"We shall kill hundreds—nay, thousands—if necessary, to keep our colony free of heretics and blasphemers," he replied angrily. "Take her away!"

So I was returned to the gaol. As I entered, Edward Wanton thrust a paper into my hands. "Governor Endecott bids you read this letter to him from your husband. Hearken to his plea and turn aside from this rash course. Your son is here. See him, heed him, I beg you."

But I only shook my head gently, for I grow weary of explaining that I must give pain to my family and friends so that other families and other friends may be spared similar pain in times to come.

What a dear, sweet letter is this from Will, pleading humbly for my life; and what it must have cost my proud husband to beg so of these wicked men!

[*Fourth month, First*]

The warm, bright sun has long been up, piercing the chinks of our window-boarding. I only want to complete my journal. Then I shall be ready. Let my last words be to the Lord, who has led me through this life and now leads me into the life eternal:

"Bless the Lord, O my soul; and all that is within me, bless his holy name. Bless the Lord, O my soul, and forget not all his benefits: who forgiveth all thine iniquities; who healeth all thy diseases; who redeemeth thy life from destruction; who crowneth thee with loving-kindness and tender mercies . . . ."

✤ ✤ ✤

The old man sighed and moved painfully in his chair. He recalled the day his son returned with the news of Mary's tragic, yet triumphant death:

"Mother climbed the ladder, calm and unafraid. Thy letter had great effect with the magistrates, for even then they offered to spare her life if she would but take it. But she replied, 'Nay, I cannot, for in obedience to the will of the Lord I came, and in his will I abide faithful to my death.'

"John Wilson strode forward and cried, 'Mary Dyer, repent! O repent, and be not so deluded and carried away by the deceit of the Devil!'

" 'Nay, man, I am not now to repent. But I do earnestly pray the Lord's forgiveness for them who do this from ignorance; but the Lord will punish them who do it willfully.'

"Then others cried, 'Will you have the elders pray for you?'

"She chided them gently, 'I know never an elder here.'

" 'Will you have anyone pray?'

" 'I desire the prayers of all the people of God.'

"A voice rose from the crowd: 'It may be she thinks there are none of them here either.'

"Mother, looking about, replied, 'I know but few here.'

"The voice sneered, 'You said you were in Paradise.'

"And Mother answered, 'Yea, I have been in Paradise these several days.' Then she nodded to the executioner.

"When it was over, they cast her body into a rough grave beneath the elm. As I turned away, John Taylor clasped my hand and murmured, 'She even shined in the image of God. She has gone into eternal life and glory forever.' "

And so, mused the old man, as Charles II ascended to the throne of England, Mary Dyer ascended to the throne of God—he of noble birth, she of noble spirit.

One more Quaker, William Leddra, was hanged for his uncompromising and unfaltering loyalty to God and cause before Charles intervened. Then the king chose Samuel Shattuck as his personal messenger to bear the royal orders to Massachusetts.

When the old Quaker, hat firmly set about his ears, confronted Governor Endecott, the governor's servant angrily hurled the hat to the floor; but when Sam coolly produced his royal credentials, the servent picked up the hat, brushed it carefully, and gently replaced it on the white locks; and John Endecott, raging yet fearful, bowed low.

Now Samuel Winthrop and Captain Wanton are Quakers, and thousands of others here, while those who opposed them have mellowed or died. Dead are friend and foe alike: Harry Vane and Hugh Peter, both beheaded by the state they loved and served, and John Wilson and John Norton.

A few of us remain—gentle Roger Williams, Will Coddington, Nicholas Easton, William Brenton. Why was it given us to linger for so long, while my dear wife lived only half our span? Our lives have been good and honorable; we did our duty as we saw it, with prudence and wisdom. But she lived boldly, giving herself freely, recklessly, joyously, at last giving even her life to that great cause.

Sometimes it seems to me 'twas she who showed the greater wisdom.